כֹּה עָשׂוּ חֲכָמֵינוּ

❧❧❧❧❧❧❧❧❧❧❧❧❧

Our Sages
showed the way

כֹּה עָשׂוּ חֲכָמֵינוּ

❈❈❈❈❈❈❈❈❈❈❈❈❈❈❈❈❈❈❈❈❈❈

Translated from the Hebrew by
Esther Falk
Illustrated by
Naama Nothman

VOLUME ONE

YOCHEVED SEGAL

OUR SAGES SHOWED THE WAY

*Stories for young readers and listeners
from the Talmud, Midrash,
and the literature of the Sages*

FELDHEIM PUBLISHERS

Jerusalem • New York

Originally published in Hebrew as
Ko asu chachomeinu
Copyright © 1976 by Moreshet
Tel Aviv, Israel

First English edition 1979
Second, revised edition 1982
Third printing 1988
ISBN 0-87306-289-2

Composed by computerized phototypesetting at the Feldheim Press
Designed by Charles Wengrov

Philipp Feldheim Inc.
200 Airport Executive Park
Spring Valley, NY 10977

Feldheim Publishers Ltd.
POB 6525 / Jerusalem, Israel

Printed in Israel

Author's preface to the English edition

To our readers, young ones and grownups alike:
Shalom!

With thanks to God in our heart, we are glad that this book is at last in your hands. Ever since it first appeared in Hebrew here in the Land of Israel, seventeen years ago, there has been a pressing request to have it translated into English. Parents in other lands have wanted it for their children, teachers for their pupils, Israeli children for their relatives and friends in English-speaking countries.

But as our Sages (blessed be their memory) said, "Everything depends on its own *mazal* (luck), even a Torah-scroll in the Holy Ark" (*Zohar, naso* 134). And so it was not until now that the translation could actually appear.

You might ask, "But why do we need this book? Don't we have enough books to read? There are hundreds, perhaps thousands, of children's books — and good ones, too!"

Of course, that is quite true. But then, you should know that this is not an ordinary children's book, even if it looks like one and was written especially for young readers. "What does that mean?" you wonder. Please let me explain:

Our book contains forty-three *aggadoth*, stories told us by our Sages of blessed memory. Many of them were written in the Talmud (*Bavli* and *Yerushalmi*).

5

That means they are part of the *Torah she-be'al peh,* that part of the Torah which was handed down by word of mouth from Rabbi to disciple (pupil) and was written down only much later. Other *aggadoth* were gathered by some of our Sages in such important books as *Midrash Rabbah, Yalkut Shimoni* and *Midrash Tanchuma.*

So you see, these stories are not new. Your own father and mother may have read them when they were young.

Now our Sages, of blessed memory, never meant to tell us some nice and interesting stories just to entertain and make us happy. Every story, even every phrase and almost every word were meant to teach us Torah; to explain something difficult; to make us better, wiser people; to show us how our forefathers and our great leaders and teachers fulfilled the *mitzvoth,* the commandments of God.

For example, they wanted to teach us how to honor our father and mother; how to love our fellowmen; how to love God and pray to Him; and to be gentle and helpful to His creatures; how to trust Him and not to despair even in danger; how to learn Torah with awe and love, and to work honestly; and so on.

So if you are a parent or a teacher who tells the *aggadoth* of our Sages you are actually teaching Torah; and if you are a young person reading this book or listening to the stories, you are learning Torah. And that is quite a different thing from merely reading a children's book, isn't it?

"But," you may ask now, "will the children like it?

Perhaps there are some children who do not like to listen and to learn. And will they understand? Most *aggadoth* have deep meanings, even mysterious ones, which only great scholars can understand. None is so simple as it might seem at first. Perhaps they might be too difficult for children altogether? Will they have any influence then, as our Sages intended they should? As we all know, children are much more impressed by actions than by words."

Believe me, I myself was quite troubled by such questions when I was asked by the Israeli Ministry of Education, many years ago, to write *aggadoth* in such a manner that even children in the kindergarten would be able to understand them. In fact, I was almost afraid to try. But then I knew this was important work. The thoughts of our Sages, blessed be their memory, *had* to reach our children. And I knew in my heart that it could be done, because our Torah is alive forever. It is fitting forever and for all ages.

So I began the work with awe and love. I began to learn and to write, using the explanations of our great Sages and scholars such as Rashi, consulting our learned instructors (*talmidey chachamim*), trying not to change any important detail in the *aggadoth*, but only to write them in simple and understandable language.

Now, as I mentioned, our Sages did not just tell a story nor did they use any unnecessary words. They wrote in a very short and concentrated way. Therefore, they did not tell us, for example, exactly how Bar-Kamtza looked and felt when he was chased away

Author's preface

so rudely from the party (see the story on page 65) or what the lost jewels of the Roman queen were (see the story on page 84). Such details they left for us to imagine — and so I did. Sometimes I also found it necessary to add some explanation into the story, if it was too difficult to understand otherwise. Therefore, it became impossible that there should be no differences whatever between the *aggadoth* in this book and their originals in the sources.

Now, if you are a grownup or a big boy or girl, and you want to know just how a certain *aggadah* was told by our Sages, you might be interested to look up its source. You will find the source listed at the end of each story. Sometimes there are even several sources that you might look up. I'm sure you will learn a lot if you do! (Let me include here a plea to our very young readers: Please remember that this is no ordinary book, and try to keep it clean and whole, as befitting a book with stories from our Sages of blessed memory!)

"All right," you might say now, "that's how you dealt with the problem. But what about the children in the Land of Israel? Did they understand? Did they love the stories? And did they grow to be better persons, better members of the Jewish people?"

Well, as for the children, till now several tens of thousands of them (may they multiply) have read the book in Hebrew, and many more have heard the stories told them by their parents or their teachers, or from the radio, which has broadcast many of them. And not only once did they read or listen, but many times, as they and their parents keep telling us, until they knew them almost by heart. So what do you think: Did they understand them, and did they love them?

If the *aggadoth* have helped somebody to be better, I really don't know for sure. That takes perhaps more than mere admiration and respect for our great Sages, more than merely reading and even knowing how one *should* be and act. But — shouldn't you at least give it a try?

And may God help you to succeed and send you His blessings!

Yocheved Segal

Jerusalem
Tammuz 5739 (June 1979)

EDITOR'S NOTE

There are many collections of *midreshei chazal* available, but none has been more successful or popular than Yocheved Segal's *Ko Asu Chachameinu*. The English translation of Volumes I and II, entitled *Our Sages Showed the Way*, has also met with wide acclaim. When it became obvious that a second printing of Volume I would soon be necessary, it was decided to produce a completely revised edition which would enhance the stories even more, and make the reading smoother and more enjoyable.

We hope you will agree that this second, revised edition of Volume I has indeed fulfilled this goal, and we look forward to the publication of the remaining two volumes in the series.

contents

1

Trust in Hashem

Trust in Hashem

In a faraway city there lived a very wealthy man. He had a large home with expensive furniture and a lovely garden full of flowers and trees. He could afford to buy whatever his heart desired. But in spite of all his wealth, he was not happy, for he lived alone in his big house. He had no family — neither father nor mother, wife nor children. The man was very lonely and sad.

"What good is all my money?" he thought. "Shall I buy food? I already have more than I can eat! Shall I buy more clothes? All my closets are full of clothes! Shall I buy jewelry? Alas, there is no one to enjoy it. When I die, who will inherit all my wealth? If only I were able to make someone happy with it!"

And so the man was always sad and worried. His neighbors saw that he was unhappy, and after finding out why, they said, "Why don't you give some of your money to the poor? You will make them happy and at the same time you will be doing one of the *mitzvoth* of the Torah."

The rich man decided to follow their suggestion. "Yes, that's what I'll do!" he said. "But I won't give my money to just any beggar on the street. I will only give it to someone as lonely as I, someone who doesn't have anyone else in the world to help him. Someone like that will certainly be very happy with my help."

The man took a large purse filled with silver coins and went looking among the poor for someone who lived alone and had no one to support him. But such a person was not to be found. One man was helped by his children, a second was supported by his relatives, a third person was helped by his neighbors, and a fourth by good people who fulfilled the *mitzvah* of giving *tzedakah* to the poor. The rich man searched and searched but could not find a single person who was all alone in the world and really had no one to help him.

One day, while walking in the countryside, the rich man saw a poor stranger sitting on a pile of stones. The man was very thin and his clothes were torn and shabby, yet he appeared to be happy and satisfied.

"Why are you sitting here?" asked the rich man.

"Because I have no other place to sit," replied the stranger. "I don't have a house or even a room of my own."

"Why is your face so thin?" asked the rich man.

"I have not had anything to eat for a long time," was the reply.

"Why are your clothes so shabby?"

"Because they are old and I have no other clothes," answered the beggar.

"Don't you have any relatives or neighbors or friends to help you?"

"No, I don't," said the poor man.

"At long last, I have found the man I have been looking for," thought the rich man with relief. "There is no one to help him, so I will give him my money!"

He took his purse and gave it to the stranger who stared at it in amazement and asked, "Why are you giving me so much money? If you want to give *tzedakah*, there are many other poor people in the city besides me. Why are you giving all your money to me?"

"Because I will only give my money to someone who has no one else in the whole world to help him, and you are such a person," explained the rich man.

The poor man immediately returned the purse to the rich man and exclaimed, "God forbid! I never said such a thing! There may not be any *person* in the world to help me, but *Hashem* will have pity on me and will help me. I am sure of that. Please take your money back and give it to someone else."

The rich man was disappointed. "In that case, there is no one to whom I can give my wealth!" he thought. So he dug a hole in the ground, buried his purse and returned home.

Hashem, who is aware of everything, saw that the rich man had hidden his wealth, so that no one could enjoy it. He was not pleased with this deed, and so He caused the rich man to lose all his money and become poor. At first he was forced to sell his beautiful garden and his expensive furniture. Next he had to sell his big house and everything in it, until finally he had nothing left.

Then one day he remembered the purse that he had hidden in the ground, and he thought to himself, "I will go and take that money for myself. How lucky I am that I still have something left!" So he went to the place where he had hidden his purse, but while he was digging, two policemen passed by and saw him.

"Why are you digging here?" they asked the man.

"I am looking for my money which I hid in the ground," he said.

"*Your* money, you say!" exclaimed one of the policemen. "You surely must have stolen it. Otherwise you would not have hidden it. Come with us to the city mayor and he will decide what to do with you!" So the policemen took the man and brought him before the mayor.

The man cried bitterly. "Please believe me, your honor," he pleaded. "This is truly my money and I did not steal it. I hid it only because I couldn't find anyone who deserved it."

The mayor looked at the poor man and said kindly, "Don't you recognize me? I am that same poor man who did not want to accept your money. Now you can see that *Hashem* can help everyone — even a poor man who has nothing. He had pity on me and helped me, and I became the ruler of the city. I am blessed with all that my heart desires. Fear not," added the kind mayor. "I know that you are not a thief and that the purse is yours. You may take it. But why should you remain so lonely and sad? Come live with me in my beautiful home and eat with me at my table!"

The man accepted the mayor's invitation and moved into his home. He learned to be happy and content, trusting in *Hashem* and awaiting His help.

Source: Rabbi Nissim Gaon, *Sefer Hama'asiyoth*

Everything Hashem
does is for the best

nce, Rabbi Akiva went on a long journey. He took a donkey, a rooster, and a candle along with him. He took the donkey so that he could ride on it when he was tired, and so that it could carry his packages for him. Why did he take the rooster? So that it would wake him at dawn with its familiar call. And he took the candle so that when night came, he could study Torah by the light of the burning flame.

Early one morning, Rabbi Akiva arose, said the morning prayers, and went on his way. He traveled all day long, and when the sun set and it became quite dark, he came to a town where he wanted to spend the night. But there was no inn to be found in the town, and when Rabbi Akiva asked if he could stay at someone's house for the night, the townspeople said, "We have no room for you. Travel on!"

Rabbi Akiva stood outside in the dark and cold, and no one invited him in. Yet in spite of that, he said, "Whatever *Hashem* does is for the best."

He did not want to remain in a city which was so evil that no one would invite a stranger into their home, so he went out into the fields. He found a place to sleep under a tree; he lit his candle, fed his donkey and rooster, and then sat down to study Torah. He was so absorbed in his studies that he forgot he was all alone in a field in the dark of night.

Suddenly Rabbi Akiva heard a terrible roar, and he saw a big lion jump out of the nearby forest and attack the donkey. He was still standing frightened and bewildered when a cat suddenly appeared and pounced on the rooster. And before he had a chance to save the rooster from the cat, a gust of wind blew out his candle and left him standing in complete darkness!

Rabbi Akiva had nothing left. The donkey was gone; the rooster was dead; and the candle was out. But even then Rabbi Akiva said, "Whatever *Hashem* does is for the best."

Then he heard cries for help and loud shouting from the nearby city where he had wanted to stay. What was happening there?

That very night, enemies had attacked the city and had taken all the people prisoner. They had even passed through the field where Rabbi Akiva was staying, but in the dark they could not see him, and so his life was spared.

Rabbi Akiva realized what had happened and

he said, "Now everyone can see that whatever *Hashem* does is for the best. If the lion had not devoured the donkey, it would have brayed; if the cat hadn't eaten the rooster, it would have crowed; and if the wind had not put out the candle, it would have lit up the darkness. Then the soldiers would have found me and taken me prisoner, too."

Rabbi Akiva thanked *Hashem* for saving him and he went on his way in peace.

Source: Talmud Bavli, Berachoth 60b

Nachum Ish Gam-zu

any years ago, there lived a wise and pious man in Israel whose name was Nachum Ish Gam-zu. Why was he called Gam-zu? Because whenever anything happened, he always said, *"Gam zu letovah*—this too is for the best. Whatever *Hashem* does, He does for the best!"

It happened once that the Jewish people in Eretz Yisrael said, "We shall send a gift to the king of the Romans, so that he will not make war on us!"

And so they did. They filled a box full of precious stones and pearls, a present for the Roman king. But who would guard the precious stones on the long journey from Eretz Yisrael to Rome? The road was dangerous. There might be a storm at sea, or thieves might steal the box. Where could they find an honest and trustworthy man to carry the gems to the king?

Then they thought of Nachum Ish Gam-zu. "We will send him!" they said.

Nachum agreed to take the box to the king

because he wanted to help his people. He started on the long and dangerous journey, unafraid. "This, too, is for the best," he repeated to himself.

Nachum Ish Gam-zu traveled on a ship for many days, and then he walked on foot all day long until he reached an inn where he could stop to rest for the night.

Nachum said his prayers and lay down to sleep, for he was very, very tired. He put the box with the jewels on the bed beside him.

The innkeeper saw the beautiful box. He was very curious, and he wanted to know what was in it. So when Nachum Ish Gam-zu fell asleep, the innkeeper came over quietly and opened the box. How the precious stones sparkled! The innkeeper looked long and hard at the treasure. "How I would like to have such a treasure!" he thought. And then he did something very evil — he removed the pearls and the precious stones and put dirt and pebbles in their place. Then he closed the box carefully and went to sleep.

Nachum Ish Gam-zu woke up early the next morning. He said his prayers, took his box and went to the king's palace.

When he came before the king, Nachum said, "Greetings, Your Majesty! I have brought you a beautiful gift from the Jews of Eretz Yisrael."

The king saw the lovely box. With great anticipation, he opened it. What did he find? Dirt!

Dirt and a few small stones. The king's face flushed with anger.

"What is this?" he called out. "Do you call this a beautiful gift? Don't I have enough dirt and stones in my own courtyard? I see that the Jews are making fun of me!" he shouted. "I will punish them, and the man who brought the box will be put to death at once!"

But Nachum Ish Gam-zu was not afraid. Again he said, "This, too, is for the best. Whatever *Hashem* does is for the best!"

Hashem saw that Nachum had trust in Him, and so He sent Eliyahu Hanavi (the Prophet Elijah) to save him. Eliyahu disguised himself as one of the princes and came to the king.

"Why are you angry, Your Majesty?" he asked the king. "This is certainly not plain dirt. Why would the Jews want to make you angry? Maybe there is a secret in this dirt. Let us throw some of it into the air. Perhaps it will turn into swords and arrows and we will be able to conquer the king's enemies in the same way that Avraham, the father of the Jewish people, conquered his enemies."

The king thought for a moment. "Very well," he said. "Let us try!"

So they threw some of the dirt into the air, and behold! The dirt turned into swords and arrows! And with these weapons, the king conquered his enemies.

27

The king was overjoyed. He said to Nachum Ish Gam-zu, "Please forgive me for being angry at you. You have brought me a very worthy gift indeed. Now I will fill your box with gold and pearls in place of the wondrous soil that you have brought me. And please thank the Jewish people for me."

Nachum took the box filled with precious stones and returned happily to Eretz Yisrael. "I have always said that everything that happens is for the best!" he said.

Source: Talmud Bavli, Ta'anith 21a

An uninterrupted prayer

 Jewish man once went on a long journey. After a while the man saw that it was time to say his prayers, but there was no *beith knesseth* to be found, and there were no houses nearby. He was surrounded by open fields. So he stood in one of the fields by the side of the road and prayed.

When he reached the *Shemoneh Esreh*, a Roman nobleman passed by. (The *Shemoneh Esreh* is a prayer that you say quietly while standing, and you are not allowed to interrupt the prayer by speaking in the middle.) The prince came riding by on a horse with his followers behind him and his servants running ahead to clear the way. All the people who passed by the prince greeted him respectfully and honored him. His subjects were afraid of him, for they knew that if they did not act respectfully, they would be punished.

The Roman saw the Jewish man standing in the field engrossed in his prayers. He was saying the *Shemoneh Esreh* so intently that he did not

The prince was angry,
yet he waited
and did not interrupt the man's prayer.

even look up. The prince called out a greeting, but the man did not answer. The prince was angry, yet he waited and did not interrupt the man's prayer. But the moment the Jew finished, the prince shouted, "Fool! Do you not see who is passing by? How dare you not greet me! If I had stabbed you with my sword, who would have saved you?" Then he paused, looked at the bewildered man, and finished with a threat. "I will punish you severely!" he exclaimed in anger.

"Please, please wait!" pleaded the God-fearing man. "Perhaps if I explain what I was doing, you will not be angry," he said.

The Roman listened.

"Tell me, Your Highness," asked the Jew, "have you ever stood before the king?"

"Certainly," answered the nobleman proudly. "I have stood before the king many times!"

"Well," asked the Jew, "if a simple man, or even another prince, should pass by while you are in the presence of the king, and if he should greet you, would you stop to answer him?" he asked.

"Heaven forbid!" answered the Roman. "It is not permissible to speak to anyone while standing before the king. This would be a grave insult to His Majesty!"

"What would the king do to you if you interrupted your audience with him to greet someone?" asked the Jewish man.

31

Trust in Hashem

"He would kill me," answered the prince.

"Do you see?" explained the man. "I was standing in prayer before the King of all kings, *Hakadosh Baruch Hu.* How could I stop to greet you?"

The Roman thought for a moment. "You are right!" he said. "I can understand now why you did not greet me."

The Roman was no longer angry. He did not punish the Jew, and he allowed him to continue his journey in peace.

Source: Talmud Bavli, Berachoth 32b

2

The beith hamikdash

The beith hamikdash in its glory

When the *beith hamikdash* was standing in the holy city of Yerushalayim, there was not another building in the world to rival its beauty. It was built of huge stones, wonderfully cut, and part of it was covered with blue-green marble that resembled the waves of the sea. Most of the gates were made of gold, and the altar for incense was covered with gold.

The Jewish people went up to the *beith hamikdash* in Yerushalayim three times a year — on Pesach, on Shavuoth and on Sukkoth. They came from all the cities, towns and villages of Eretz Yisrael, and no matter how many came, there was always room for everyone in the three large courtyards, one of which was the "women's court."

The holiest place of all was the *kodesh hakodashim*. Two ark curtains, woven with blue, purple, scarlet and golden threads, were hung at the entrance, and no one was allowed to enter the *kodesh hakodashim* except for the *kohen gadol* on Yom Kippur.

The beith hamikdash

There were many *menoroth* in the *beith hamikdash*, all made of pure gold and decorated with golden flowers and buttons. There were also many other gold and silver vessels, so many that it was almost impossible to count them.

There was a vine in the *beith hamikdash* which looked just like a real vine with leaves and grapes, but it too was made of gold. Anyone who wanted to bring a gift brought a gold leaf, or berry, or cluster of grapes, and hung it on the gold vine. The *kohanim* would gather these gifts and use them for the *beith hamikdash*.

There were two special rooms set aside — one for *tzedakah*, and one for vessels. The *tzedakah* room was called the "secret chamber" because good men brought money in secret and left it there. The poor could take as much of this money as they needed. No one would know, and they did not have to feel ashamed because they were taking charity.

The second room was called the "chamber for vessels." If anyone wanted to donate a vessel to the *beith hamikdash*, he brought it to this room, and the *kohanim* used these vessels when they needed them.

There were three steps leading from one courtyard — the *ezrath yisrael* — to the second — the *ezrath kohanim*. Above the courtyards was a platform where the *leviim* stood and sang *tehillim*,

King David's Psalms, while the sacrifices were offered on the big stone altar.

On the six intermediate days of Sukkoth, during the celebration of the *simchath beith hasho'evah*, the *leviim* stood on the fifteen steps that led from the women's court to the *ezrath yisrael* and raised their voices in song.

They had lyres, flutes, cymbals, and many other ancient musical instruments which we no longer have today. Their songs and music were very beautiful.

People from all over the world came to see the beauty and the glory of the *beith hamikdash*. The Jewish people loved it not only for its splendor. They loved it because they prayed there to their Father in Heaven, to the Holy One, blessed be He. They brought their sacrifices to the *beith hamikdash* and Hashem answered their prayers. He forgave their sins and He sent them endless blessings. Whoever entered the *beith hamikdash* came out contented and happy.

All this was when the *beith hamikdash* was in existence. And now that we have neither the *beith hamikdash* nor the *kodesh hakodashim*, nor the golden altar for incense, nor the stone altar for sacrifices, where shall we pray?

Instead of the *beith hamikdash*, we have *batei knesseth*. They are like small "temples" where we pray and ask *Hashem* to forgive our sins, to send

37 🌺

us a good year, to make all the sick people well, and to bring the *mashiach* soon. And if we are worthy, He will rebuild the *beith hamikdash* as of old and the new Temple will be even more beautiful and more splendid than the one which was destroyed.

Sources: Jerusalem Talmud, Shekalim 5:4
Talmud Bavli, Sukkah 51
Talmud Bavli, Baba Bathra 4
Talmud Bavli, Tamid 29
Josephus, *The Wars of the Jews,* chapter 55
Josephus, *Antiquities,* chapter 8

Yom Kippur in the beith hamikdash

ow was Yom Kippur celebrated in Yerushalayim when the *beith hamikdash* was still standing?

One week before Yom Kippur, the *kohen gadol* walked to the *beith hamikdash* in a great procession. All of the people in the city came to watch him or accompany him.

First came the king and the princes, followed by the *leviim*, all wearing blue robes of silk. Next came *kohanim* wearing white robes, and then the singers, the musicians, the trumpeters, and all the other people who worked in the *beith hamikdash*—including the gatekeepers who guarded the gates and the repairmen. The rabbis walked near the *kohen gadol* while *kohanim* holding golden staves helped keep the road clear. Last of all came the *kohen gadol* himself with all of the older and most important *kohanim*.

When they reached the *beith hamikdash*, they began to pray. The thousands of voices were so powerful that the birds flying over Yerushalayim almost fell to the ground from fright.

*Escorting the kohen gadol
to the beith hamikdash*

On the night of Yom Kippur, the *kohen gadol* stayed awake all night long. The other *kohanim* sat and learned Torah with him so that he would not fall asleep. When the day dawned, he put on golden robes and offered the first sacrifice which had to be brought on Yom Kippur. Before he went into the *kodesh hakodashim* where only the *kohen gadol* was permitted to enter, he removed his golden clothes and put on a white robe which made him look like an angel of God. He prayed to *Hashem* and asked Him to forgive the Jewish people and to inscribe them for a good year.

The entire day, the *kohanim* and the *leviim* and all the people stood silently, watching the sacrifices and the prayers of the *kohen gadol*. And when the *kohen gadol* prayed and uttered the name of *Hashem*, they all bowed down to the ground and called out, "Blessed be the name of the glory of His kingdom forever and ever."

How wonderful it was to watch the *kohen gadol* come out of the *kodesh hakodashim*! It was like seeing a king wearing a crown. The people did not once feel hungry or thirsty or tired.

There was a red ribbon tied at the entrance to the *beith hamikdash*. In the evening, at the close of Yom Kippur, the people watched the red ribbon turn white as snow. This was the sign that *Hashem* had forgiven them their sins.

When Yom Kippur was over, no one rushed

The beith hamikdash

home to eat. First they took flaming torches and
escorted the *kohen gadol* to his home. Everyone
was eager to come forward and to greet him on the
way. All the windows in the houses were decorated
with garlands of flowers, beautiful tapestries, and
embroidered cloths, because the people were
happy and grateful to have been forgiven by God.
Fortunate were those who saw this wonderful
sight!

Sources: Yom Kippur Machzor
Eliahu Kitov, *The Book of Our Heritage*
Mishnah Yoma, 1-7

🌺 42

The celebration of the Drawing of Water

ur Sages, of blessed memory, said, "One who has never seen this joy [the ceremony of the Drawing of the Water] has never witnessed joy in his life." What was this celebration?

On the second night of the Festival of Sukkoth, all the people went to the *beith hamikdash*. The sons of the *kohanim* climbed up on ladders to the golden candelabras, filled the cups with oil and lit them. How bright they were—bright enough to light up all the courtyards of Yerushalayim! Meanwhile, the *leviim* played their musical instruments and sang songs of praise to *Hashem*.

The great rabbis who taught the people Torah, the head of the Court, and the elders all danced and sang. They tossed flaming torches up in the air, catching them again and again. The head of the *sanhedrin*, Rabban Shimon ben Gamliel, used to juggle eight torches at once, tossing and catching them in turn, without having the torches touch each other. The dancing and singing and rejoicing lasted all night long.

The beith hamikdash

At daybreak, two *kohanim* blew silver trumpets. This was the signal for everyone to go to the spring of Shiloach which was not far from the *beith hamikdash*. The *kohanim* drew water from the spring and poured it into a golden bottle. Then, blowing their trumpets, they made their way back to the *beith hamikdash*. There were two silver goblets in the *beith hamikdash*. The *kohanim* filled one goblet with the water from the golden bottle, and the second goblet with wine. Then the water and the wine were poured over the altar in the *beith hamikdash*.

The *leviim* again took their instruments and played their beautiful music on their harps, cymbals and lyres. The *kohanim* sounded their horns, and the people bowed down to the ground. Finally, they all circled the altar, carrying their *lulavim* and *ethrogim* in their hands.

When the ceremonies ended, the people returned home and ate their festival meal in gladness and rejoicing.

Sources: Talmud Bavli, Sukkah 51b
Tosefta, 4

3

Honoring one's parents

Rabbi Tarfon
and his mother

any years ago there lived a great rabbi who was both wise and good. He had learned the entire Torah and many students came from afar to study with him. People loved him for his goodness and respected him for his great learning. His name was Rabbi Tarfon.

Rabbi Tarfon had a very old mother who became ill. She was so weak that she could hardly climb into or out of her bed. Rabbi Tarfon's servants and his many students could all have helped the old lady, but Rabbi Tarfon would not let them. He wanted to honor his mother and to care for her himself. Every time she wished to get in or out of bed, he hurried to her bedside, bent down to the floor and let her step on his back. He helped her climb in and out of bed the same way every day.

One Shabbath his mother was feeling a little better. She called Rabbi Tarfon and said to him, "Tarfon, my son, I would like to take a short walk in the courtyard." Rabbi Tarfon was happy that his mother was feeling well enough to go for a walk.

After being indoors for so long, the old woman enjoyed the fresh air. She warmed herself in the sun and was delighted with the flowers and the song of the birds. But in the middle of her walk, the strap on her sandal tore, and the sandal fell off. Rabbi Tarfon was upset.

"My mother cannot walk without her sandal," he thought, "and we cannot repair it on Shabbath. How will she return home? She can't walk barefoot. She is so old and frail that she might catch a cold walking on the ground."

Then he had an idea. He bent down, stretched out his hands, and had his mother walk on his hands instead of on the cold ground. She walked all the way back to the house on the palms of his hands. When she arrived home, she lay down to rest.

Some time later, Rabbi Tarfon wasn't feeling well. When his friends, the rabbis, came to visit him, his old mother said to them, "Please pray for Rabbi Tarfon, my son, for he gives me too much respect."

"Why?" asked the rabbis. "What does he do for you?"

The old mother told them the story of her torn sandal and how her son had let her walk on his hands.

Rabbi Tarfon and his mother

On hearing the story, the rabbis said, "That
was truly an act of kindness. But even if he had
done a thousand times more for you, he still would
not have completely fulfilled all of the *mitzvah*,
'Honor your father and your mother.'"

Sources: Jerusalem Talmud, Pe'ah, chapter 1
Talmud Bavli, Kiddushin 31b

49 ❧

Respect for a father

In the time of the *beith hamikdash* the *kohen gadol* wore beautiful robes. And on his chest he wore the *choshen*—a breastplate studded with twelve precious jewels, one for each of the twelve tribes of Israel. It happened that one of the jewels was lost, and the *chachamim* collected a large sum of gold to buy a new stone. They went around to many cities and asked, "Where can we buy the kind of jewel — as big and as beautiful as the lost stone — which we need for the *choshen* of the *kohen gadol*?" But no one knew.

At last they met a man who said, "In the city of Ashkelon, there is a very wealthy man whose name is Dama ben Nethina. He has the most beautiful gems and pearls in the land."

So the rabbis went to the home of Dama ben Nethina in Ashkelon and knocked on his door. Dama came out, and seeing the honored visitors, said, "Welcome, great rabbis! What is it you want? What can I do for you?"

The rabbis answered, "We have heard that you

sell precious stones, and we are interested in buying one from you. We will pay you one hundred coins of gold for the stone we need." And they described the stone to him.

Dama ben Nethina listened politely and said, "Please come into my house. Wait a moment and I will bring you a stone just like the one you described."

Dama went to the box where he kept his jewels, but the box was locked and the keys were not in their usual place. Dama went into his father's room to look for the keys. He saw his father fast asleep on the bed, and the keys for the box lay under his pillow.

Dama thought, "If I pull the keys out from under the pillow, I might wake my father up. He might be upset, or perhaps frightened, at being awakened suddenly. No, I must not bother him."

Dama returned to the waiting rabbis and said quietly, "I cannot bring you the stone you want because my father has the keys to the box of jewels and he is sleeping."

The rabbis thought that Dama was inventing an excuse because he wanted more money for the jewel, so they said, "Very well, we will give you two hundred coins of gold instead of the one hundred we promised!"

But Dama was determined. "No," he said, "I cannot wake my father up!"

"We need this jewel very urgently. We will pay you three hundred gold coins," insisted the rabbis.

But Dama ben Nethina refused. Even when the rabbis offered him one thousand pieces of gold, he didn't change his mind. "I will not wake my father up for all the money in the world," he declared. When the rabbis realized that Dama would not sell them the jewel, they went away, very disappointed.

Soon after, Dama ben Nethina's father awoke from his sleep. Dama took the keys and opened the box. He took out the stone and hurried to find the rabbis. When he caught up with the wise men and gave them the stone, their disappointment turned to joy. They wanted to pay him one thousand gold pieces, but Dama would not accept that much money.

"Pay me one hundred pieces of gold," he said to them. "That is what you offered me in the beginning. I don't want to be paid more for honoring my father."

"See how Dama ben Nethina honors his father," said the rabbis. "We can all learn a great lesson from him!"

Sources: Jerusalem Talmud, Pe'ah, chapter 1
Talmud Bavli, Kiddushin 31a

Rabbi Yehoshua
and the butcher

very wise man lived in Eretz Yisrael. His name was Rabbi Yehoshua. Everyone called him "the Light of Israel" because he enlightened the whole world with his wisdom and his knowledge of Torah.

One night Rabbi Yehoshua had a dream. In his dream he heard a voice saying, "How fortunate you are, Rabbi Yehoshua! When you come to *gan eden* in the World to Come, you will dwell together with Nannas the butcher, because your reward in *gan eden* is equal to his."

Rabbi Yehoshua awoke from his sleep and thought, "How strange! All my life I have studied the Torah and obeyed the *mitzvoth*. I have eighty students to whom I teach Torah from morning till night, and yet in the end, my reward is the same as that of a simple, unknown butcher."

Rabbi Yehoshua was unhappy. In the morning he called his students and said to them, "Let us go and look for Nannas the butcher. I want to meet the man who will be my companion in *gan eden*."

Rabbi Yehoshua and his disciples went from city to city and from village to village, and everywhere he asked, "Does Nannas the butcher live here?"

At last he came to one town where the people said, "Nannas the butcher? Yes, he lives in this city. But what do you want with him? You are very wise and very righteous. What do you want with someone as simple as Nannas?"

But Rabbi Yehoshua repeated his request. "Please, would you invite him to come see me?"

So the people went to the butcher and said, "Rabbi Yehoshua has asked that you come to see him immediately."

Nannas thought they were making fun of him. "You are mocking me! How is it possible that a great and wise rabbi would want to speak to me? I will not go," he declared. "You only want to embarrass me!"

The people returned to Rabbi Yehoshua with the reply. "Nannas does not want to come to you! Now you can see that it is not worth your while to speak to someone like him."

But instead, Rabbi Yehoshua himself went to the butcher. When Nannas saw Rabbi Yehoshua, he was awed by the great man. He bowed down and asked, "Why has the rabbi come to visit me? How do I deserve such a great honor? You are so righteous and so wise. Everyone calls you the Light

Rabbi Yehoshua went to see Nannas the butcher.

of Israel, while I am just a simple, uneducated butcher."

"Tell me," said Rabbi Yehoshua, "what do you do when you are not busy working in the butcher shop?"

"I have an old father and mother," Nannas answered. "They are sick and helpless. Every day I dress them, feed them and wash them, and I do all I can to help them."

Rabbi Yehoshua stood up, kissed the butcher's head and said, "How sweet and pleasant are your deeds! You fulfill the commandment 'Honor your father and your mother.' How fortunate am I that I am worthy to be your companion in *gan eden*!"

Source: Seder Hadoroth

The boy and the king

There once lived an old man and his wife who loved both the Torah and all the children who studied it. They were very unhappy that they had no children of their own to sit and learn.

Every day, the old man went to meet the neighborhood children on their way home from school. He would play with them and kiss them and ask, "Tell me, what did you learn today in school?" When they told him all the things they had learned, he would sigh and say, "How lucky your parents are! How I wish that I had children like you!"

But since he had no children of his own who could learn Torah, the old man gave his money to *talmidei chachamim* so that they could sit and study the Torah all day long.

Hakadosh Baruch Hu (the Holy One, blessed be He) saw how much the fine old man loved the Torah and those who study it. He took pity on him and granted him a son. A beautiful little boy was born to the man and his wife. How delighted they

"Tell me, what did you learn today in school?"

were, and how they loved their child. One day, when the boy grew older, his father took him on his shoulders and brought him to school.

"Please teach the Torah to my son," said the father to the teacher. The teacher brought the boy into the class where he sat down with the other children and began to learn *Bereshith*—the first book in the Torah.

From that day on, the father brought his son to school every day. The child loved to learn, and soon he knew what *Hashem* had created on each day of the week.

One day the little boy said to his father, "Why must you carry me to school on your shoulders every day? Please let me go to school by myself!"

"Very well," said the old man. "You surely are old enough, so go in peace!"

And so the boy took his books and went off by himself. He was halfway to school when one of the king's noblemen passed by. When the nobleman saw the beautiful child, he said to himself, "How I would like to have such a child. I will take him and he will be mine!" He grabbed the child, pulled him up on his horse, and rode away with him to the king's palace.

That afternoon the old man and woman waited and waited for their little boy to return from school. It was getting late and still their son did not come home. The father finally went to the

59

school and asked the teacher, "Where is my son? Why hasn't he returned home yet?"

The teacher was surprised. "Your son was not in school today at all," he said.

The poor old man walked all around the town looking for his son. Everywhere he went he asked, "Have you seen my son?" But no one had. The old woman, too, searched everywhere for the child, but couldn't find him. Both the father and mother were terribly frightened and upset.

Hashem saw their sorrow, and He pitied the poor parents. What did He do? That very evening He caused the king to become ill. As he lay in his bed feeling very sick, he said to his servants, "Bring me my Book of Cures, and I will see what medicine I should take."

"Bring the Book of Cures!" a servant was commanded.

The book was brought, and *Hashem* caused a miracle to happen. The Book of Cures was changed into the Book of *Bereshith*. The king took the book and tried to read it, but he could not, because it was written in Hebrew. "This looks like a Hebrew book," said the servants to the king. "We will find a Jew who can read it to you."

They looked all over, but they could not find a Jew to read the strange book. Then the nobleman who had kidnapped the little boy said to the king, "This morning I passed through a Jewish town and

I took a child from there. Perhaps he will know how to read this book."

The child was brought to the king. "Can you read this book?" the king asked him. When the little boy recognized the Book of *Bereshith*, the same book he was studying in school, he started to cry. "What is the matter, my child?" asked the king. "Are you afraid of me?"

"No," answered the little boy. "I am not afraid. But I am thinking of my father who brought me to school to learn the Torah, and this is the book I studied. Yes, I can read this book very well."

The little boy started to read to the king. He explained everything that he read. By the time the king heard how *Hashem* had created the world, he was feeling strong enough to sit up in a chair. And when the boy finished reading how *Hashem* blessed the seventh day and made it holy, the king was feeling perfectly fine.

"If you will stay here with me," he said, "I will give you whatever your heart desires. All the toys and all the sweets in the world will be yours, because I was cured by listening to you read from the Torah!"

"All I want," answered the boy, "is to go home to my mother and father. I'm sure they are very worried because I did not return. I could never be happy without my mother and father."

"You are a good son," said the king, "and I see

that you love your parents more than the gifts I promised you. You may return home, and you may take whatever you desire as a gift from me.''

The boy chose gifts for his father and mother, and then he returned home in the king's golden coach. How happy his parents were when they saw him. They thanked *Hashem* over and over again for His help, and were happy and content forever after.

Source: Midrash Assereth Hadibroth

Respect for all people

Kamtza
and Bar-Kamtza

nsult and revenge caused the burning of our *beith hamikdash* and the destruction of Yerushalayim. It happened this way:

In the time of the *beith hamikdash*, there were many wealthy people who lived in Yerushalayim. One of these wealthy men planned a feast in honor of a happy occasion. The man invited all of his rich friends and acquaintances to come to the feast to eat, drink and rejoice with him.

This rich man had a very good friend named Kamtza. He told his servant to go to Kamtza and invite him to the feast.

The servant, however, was not paying close attention to what his master said, and he didn't hear the name clearly. And so, by mistake, he went to another man with a similar name, Bar-Kamtza, and he said, "My master invites you to the great feast he has prepared."

Now, Bar-Kamtza was not a friend of the rich man. In fact, the two men disliked each other and were always quarreling. So Bar-Kamtza was very

65

surprised to receive the invitation. "Why did he invite me?" he thought. "Perhaps he finally wants to make peace with me? In that case, I should not be angry anymore either. I shall go to his party and see."

Bar-Kamtza put on his best clothes, went to the house of the rich man, and sat down at the table among the other guests. "How wonderful it would be," he thought, "if my host really wants to make peace with me."

But it was not to be. When the host walked around greeting his guests, he looked for his good friend, Kamtza. But whom did he see? Bar-Kamtza! He became very angry, rushed over to him and shouted, "What are you doing here? Get up at once and leave my house!"

Bar-Kamtza turned white with embarrassment. With a trembling voice he whispered, "It seems that I was invited by mistake. But since I am already here, please allow me to stay. Do not chase me away in front of all your guests. I will pay for my food and drink."

But the host shouted even louder, "No! I will not have you! Get out!"

"Allow me to stay just this once," Bar-Kamtza whispered. "I will pay for half your feast."

"No, no," insisted the rich man. "I do not want your money! Leave my house at once!"

Bar-Kamtza pleaded with his host, offering to

pay for the whole feast. But the rich man would not hear of it. He seized Bar-Kamtza, pulled him out of his chair, and chased him out of the house.

Bar-Kamtza was furious. He had been cruelly insulted before all those guests, yet no one had come to his defense. Not one single person had asked the host to allow him to remain at the feast.

"I will have my revenge on them all!" declared Bar-Kamtza in his anger. "The host will bitterly regret his behavior. And the guests will be sorry that they did not help me! I shall see to it that all the magnificent houses in Yerushalayim will be burned to the ground!" In his anger, Bar-Kamtza forgot that he was included in his own curse, because if all the grand houses in Yerushalayim were to be destroyed, his own house would be among them.

What did he do? He went to the emperor who then ruled over Eretz Yisrael and said, "Your Highness, I have important information to disclose. The Jews of Jerusalem are planning a rebellion against you! They no longer want you to rule them."

The angry emperor sent out a mighty army. His soldiers arrived in Yerushalayim, burned the *beith hamikdash* and destroyed the entire city.

Source: Talmud Bavli, Gittin 55-56

Respect
for all people

or many years Shimon ben Elazar sat in a *yeshivah* and learned Torah until he became a great rabbi. Then, after being away for so long, he decided to return home to see his father and mother. He bought himself a donkey and started the journey home.

The trip was a long one. Rabbi Shimon sat comfortably upon the donkey, and as the animal plodded along, he thought to himself, "How fortunate I am to have learned so much Torah! When I arrive home, many people will want to study with me and will want me to be their teacher." Rabbi Shimon was feeling pleased with himself and very proud of his great learning.

Then he saw a stranger coming towards him down the road. As the man came nearer, Rabbi Shimon saw that he was very ugly and his clothes were dirty. The expression on his face and all his movements were very strange. Rabbi Shimon had never before seen such an unpleasant looking man, and he felt uncomfortable in his presence. Suddenly the man turned to Rabbi Shimon and called out in a gruff voice, "Greetings, Rabbi."

Rabbi Shimon was annoyed. This was not the way one greets a *talmid chacham*! Perhaps the man was trying to insult him. Not only was his face ugly, but he was impolite as well! Instead of returning a friendly greeting, Rabbi Shimon exclaimed, "You fool! How plain you are! Are all the people in your town as homely as you?"

The man was very insulted. "I don't know," he answered. "But if you don't like my appearance, go to the Craftsman who made me and tell Him, 'How ugly is the vessel that You fashioned!'"

"*Hashem* is the Craftsman who made him!" Rabbi Shimon said to himself. "Alas, what have I done to speak so foolishly?"

Rabbi Shimon was very sorry about his angry outburst. He got down from his donkey, bowed in front of the man and begged, "Forgive me for speaking so rudely to you. Please don't be angry with me."

But the man refused to listen. "I will not forgive you," he said, "until you go to my Maker and tell Him how ugly His work is." The man then turned his back on Rabbi Shimon and continued down the road.

Rabbi Shimon followed him all the way, walking after him and begging to be forgiven, but the man would not listen. At last they came to the city. Many people were waiting to welcome the rabbi. When they saw him, they rushed forward and called, "Shalom! Welcome, our rabbi, our teacher!"

"Whom are you talking to?" asked the ugly man. "Whom are you calling 'teacher and rabbi'?"

"This man who is walking behind you," answered the townspeople, "Rabbi Shimon, the son of Elazar, the great sage and scholar. He is returning home after many years of study."

"If this is a rabbi and a sage, I pray that there be no more like him in Israel!" the man said bitterly.

The people were shocked. "Explain yourself!" they demanded. So the man told them what had happened—how he had greeted Rabbi Shimon, and how Rabbi Shimon had ignored his greeting and then insulted him.

"Forgive him in spite of what he did," they replied. "Forgive him for the sake of his great learning."

"Very well," the man agreed. "I shall forgive him for your sakes, only because you have asked me to do so. And only on the condition that he will not behave this way again."

Rabbi Shimon was very grateful that the man had forgiven him. He immediately went into the *beith midrash* to teach the townspeople. And what was the first lesson he taught them?

"A man should always be as soft as a reed, not hard as a cedar tree. He must try to be pleasant to everyone — to speak softly and gently, not boastfully or arrogantly. For a proud man is like a hard tree, and everyone who comes his way gets hurt."

After this, Rabbi Shimon was very careful to follow his own teachings and not to insult anyone ever again.

Sources: Talmud Bavli, Ta'anith 20 a-b
Avoth de Rabbi Nathan, chapter 41

Rabbi Elazar
and the Roman

nce a group of Jews were going up to the *beith hamikdash* in Yerushalayim. Among them was a great and wise man whose name was Rabbi Elazar ben Shamua. As they were walking on the road along the seacoast, they saw a ship sailing slowly in the middle of the ocean.

Suddenly, a great storm arose. The waves dashed against the ship, tossing it up and down with great fury, and soon, the ship was smashed and sank to the bottom of the sea. All the people aboard drowned except for one man who held on to a large board and swam to dry land.

The man had no clothes, for he had taken them off and thrown them away in order to swim more easily. When he saw the people walking along the coast, he hid behind some rocks, embarrassed to be seen without clothes. He stuck his head out and called, "Have pity, good people! Give me some clothes! My ship sank in the sea and I was left with nothing to wear!"

The people saw that the man was a Roman.

They didn't want to help him because the cruel Romans ruled Eretz Yisrael in those days and made the Jews suffer greatly. They laughed at the Roman, and said, "May the same misfortune befall all of your people!"

The Roman did not know what to do. Then he saw Rabbi Elazar ben Shamua. Realizing that he must be an important man, he turned to him and said, "I see that you are a man who is respected for your age and wisdom. You surely know how to treat people properly. Have pity on me, I beg you, and give me something to wear."

Rabbi Elazar immediately took off his coat and gave it to the man. Then he brought him home and gave him food to eat and a place to rest, for the man was hungry and tired. Rabbi Elazar also gave the Roman some money and a horse to ride, and finally he accompanied him politely for a long stretch of his journey.

Many years later the same shipwrecked Roman became the emperor. All this time he remembered how the Jews had laughed at him in his time of trouble. Now he wanted his revenge. So he wrote a letter to the commander of his army, saying, "You are to kill all the Jews in the Land of Israel!"

When the Jews heard the terrible edict, they came to Rabbi Elazar ben Shamua and said, "Please go to the emperor and ask him to forgive us. Bring him a large gift of gold to appease him."

Rabbi Elazar agreed, took the gift of gold, and arrived at the palace gate.

"Tell the emperor that a Jewish man is at the gate and wants to see him," he said. The guards did as they were told.

"Bring him in!" ordered the emperor.

When Rabbi Elazar entered the room, the emperor immediately recognized him. And he remembered the great kindness Rabbi Elazar had shown him in his time of need. He sprang up from his chair and bowed down saying, "Welcome, Rabbi. What is your wish? Can I help you in some way? What brings you from so far?"

"I have come to ask you to forgive the Jews," said Rabbi Elazar. "Do not take revenge on them."

"They did not do as your Torah commands," the emperor answered. "They not only failed to help me, but they also laughed at me. Therefore, I will kill them!"

"Forgive my people, even if they did not treat you kindly," said Rabbi Elazar. He held out the gold to the king. "They have sent you a gift."

"I don't need their present," said the emperor, "but I will forgive them for your sake. You take the gold. I give it to you in return for the money you gave me long ago.

"And now go into my treasury and choose seventy beautiful garments in place of the coat you once gave me. Then return to your home in peace."

When Rabbi Elazar returned to Eretz Yisrael and told the Jews that the emperor had forgiven them, their joy was great.

They all thanked Rabbi Elazar. They knew that they had been saved only because of his *mitzvah* of kindness to the Roman many years before.

Source: Midrash Koheleth Rabbah, chapter 11

5

The honesty of our Sages

Rabbi Pinchas
and the beggars

any years ago, a wise and righteous man by the name of Rabbi Pinchas ben Yair lived in Eretz Yisrael. Everyone knew that he was a very good and holy man, and many people came to him for advice.

Once, two poor men came to Rabbi Pinchas ben Yair's town. They went from house to house to ask for charity. The people of the town were poor themselves and couldn't give much money, but everyone gave them some grains of barley which they could grind into flour for baking bread. And so they collected two small bags of barley.

Finally, one of the poor men said to his friend, "Let's go on to another town. We might be luckier there."

But since they didn't want to carry the two bags of barley with them, they went to Rabbi Pinchas ben Yair. "Please keep this barley for a few days," they asked. "When we return from the other town, we will take it back."

Rabbi Pinchas ben Yair took the barley from

the poor men, and they went on their way. But in the neighboring town they met with no better luck, and they decided to move on to a third town and then to a fourth. As for the barley, they forgot all about it.

Rabbi Pinchas ben Yair waited a few days, a week, a month — but the poor men did not return. An entire year passed, and Rabbi Pinchas said, "If I leave the barley in my storehouse any longer, it will either spoil or the mice will eat it up. When these poor fellows return, there will be nothing left."

So Rabbi Pinchas went out into his field. He plowed the soil and planted the grains of barley. The rains came, the seeds sprouted and a new crop of barley grew. When the grain ripened, Rabbi Pinchas harvested the crop and stored it in bigger sacks, for now there was much more grain than the two men had collected at first. Then he put the sacks away for the poor men.

But the men did not return that year either, and Rabbi Pinchas sowed the seeds and harvested the grain again. This time there was even more barley which he put into still bigger sacks. Every year Rabbi Pinchas plowed, sowed, harvested and threshed the grain. Finally, he built a storehouse to hold all the barley he had grown.

Seven years passed. The two poor men happened to return to Rabbi Pinchas's town. They were still very poor. One of them remembered that many years earlier they had left some barley at the house of Rabbi Pinchas ben Yair. "Perhaps the barley is still good," they thought. "Even if it isn't fresh, it will still be better than nothing at all."

The men came to Rabbi Pinchas and asked, "Could you please return the barley which we left with you seven years ago?"

Rabbi Pinchas recognized the poor men and greeted them warmly. "Certainly I will return the grain to you, but you will not be able to carry it yourselves. You will need donkeys and camels to take it all away."

He took them to the storage house and said, "All this came out of your two bags of barley." Rabbi Pinchas gave them all the grain without asking for any payment for his years of hard work.

The men thanked him, ate their fill and then sold the rest of the grain. Thanks to Rabbi Pinchas ben Yair, they never had to beg for charity again.

Source: Midrash Devarim Rabbah, chapter 83

An honest purchase

abbi Shimon ben Shetach was a very wise man who had many students. He did not want to accept money from his students, for our Sages (may their memory be blessed) said, "Just as the Holy One, blessed be He, gave the Torah to the Children of Israel without asking to be paid, so we must teach Torah to others without asking to be paid." Therefore, Rabbi Shimon tried to earn his living by buying bundles of flax (to make thread for cloth) and carried them on his back to the marketplace to sell.

His pupils saw that this work was very hard for Rabbi Shimon and they said to him, "Rabbi, please let us help you. We will buy you a strong, healthy donkey to carry the flax on its back."

Rabbi Shimon agreed, and they hurried to find a donkey for their teacher. Soon they met an Arab who had just the kind of donkey they wanted.

"Will you sell us your donkey?" they asked the Arab.

"Yes," he replied, "if you pay me a good price."

The students paid the Arab the price he asked, took the donkey, and returned to their teacher. On the way home, they stopped to look at the donkey more carefully, and behold—they found a surprise! A little bag was tied to the rope around the donkey's neck, and inside the bag was a precious stone!

The students were delighted, for now Rabbi Shimon would be rich. He would be able to study Torah all day long and to teach them without having to work and worry.

When they arrived at Rabbi Shimon's house, they called, "Rabbi, Rabbi, from now on, you will no longer have to wear yourself out with hard work."

"Why not?" asked Rabbi Shimon.

"Because we bought a donkey from an Arab," answered the students, "and we found a precious stone on its neck. You can sell the stone and you will have enough money to live comfortably for a long time to come."

"Did the Arab know that a precious stone was on the donkey's neck?" asked Rabbi Shimon.

"No," answered the pupils.

"Well then," said Rabbi Shimon, "I purchased the donkey, but I did not buy the precious stone." And he promptly went and returned the stone to the Arab. The Arab, impressed with Rabbi Shimon's honesty, exclaimed, "Blessed is the God

83

of the Jewish people, who commanded them to return a lost object to its owner. And blessed are the Jews who believe in their God and who observe His commandments."

Rabbi Shimon ben Shetach was satisfied. "It is better to hear an Arab blessing the God of Israel than to own all the precious stones in the world," he said.

Source: Jerusalem Talmud, Bava Metzia, chapter 2

The queen's jewels

In the city of Rome, there once lived a queen who had a splendid palace and much gold and silver. One day, while taking a walk, the queen lost her jewels. A ring decorated with diamonds, a string of pearls and a beautiful gold bracelet were all gone.

A messenger was sent through the streets of Rome, proclaiming, "The queen has lost certain precious jewels. A generous reward awaits the person who returns them within thirty days! But if anyone hides the jewels and they are found after thirty days, he will be punished by death!"

The queen hoped that the person who would find the jewels would return them quickly. But she waited in vain.

At that time, the great Rabbi Shmuel bar Susrati came to Rome, and while he was walking in the street, he happened to find the queen's jewels. But Rabbi Shmuel did not hurry to return them. He kept the jewels for thirty days and only then did he go to the queen. "Here are your jewels, Your Majesty. I found them," he said.

The queen was troubled. She was happy that her jewels had been found, but she was angry that Rabbi Shmuel had not returned them sooner. She saw that Rabbi Shmuel was a wise old man. Perhaps he had not kept her jewels intentionally. "Have you just come to Rome?" she asked him.

"No," he replied, "I have been here thirty days."

"Did you hear the proclamation about the lost jewels?" she asked.

"Yes," replied Rabbi Shmuel.

"Perhaps you did not understand it. Repeat to me what you heard," ordered the queen.

Rabbi Shmuel repeated the proclamation, "A reward awaits the person who returns the jewels within thirty days, but anyone hiding them for more than thirty days will be killed."

"In that case," said the queen, "I do not understand you at all. If you were here and you heard the proclamation clearly, and you understood what it said, why didn't you return the jewels right away?"

"I shall gladly explain the reason," answered Rabbi Shmuel. "I did not want you to think that I returned your jewels in order to earn the reward or because I was afraid of you. I returned them because *Hashem* commanded us in the Torah to return a lost article to its owner."

The queen realized that Rabbi Shmuel was an

honest and righteous man, and she said, "Blessed is the Lord, the God of Israel." And forever after, she respected Rabbi Shmuel and honored him greatly.

Source: Jerusalem Talmud, Bava Metzia, chapter 2

The lost chickens

man was once walking along the road, carrying some chickens. After a while, he sat down to rest on the doorstep of the house of Rabbi Chanina ben Dosa. He put his chickens down and thought to himself, "I will leave my chickens here while I go buy something to eat. Then I will come back to get them."

The man went to a store, but on the way back, he forgot where he had left the chickens. He looked for the house, but couldn't find it. Finally, feeling very sad, he continued on his way.

Meanwhile, the hens became very hungry and started cackling. Rabbi Chanina ben Dosa's wife heard the noise and came out to the yard. She found a bag of chickens, their legs all tied, in her doorway. The woman looked all around, but couldn't find the owner. So she took the chickens inside and showed them to Rabbi Chanina ben Dosa.

"Someone must have left these hens here, and forgot where he put them," said Rabbi Chanina.

He sat down on the doorstep
of Rabbi Chanina ben Dosa.

"We will take care of them until he comes back. Meanwhile, give them food and water. But we must not use the eggs, for the eggs belong to the owner."

And so Rabbi Chanina's wife scattered seeds in the yard and put out a dish filled with water. The chickens ate, drank, walked around the yard and laid eggs. The eggs hatched into little chicks, and the chicks grew into hens and roosters. More eggs were laid; more chickens were hatched; and soon the yard was full.

Rabbi Chanina saw that raising chickens was becoming too difficult a task for him. He was poor and hardly had enough food for his household. Where would he get feed for so many chickens? They were a bother, too. The hens disturbed his rest by their constant cackling. They pecked at the vegetables in his garden, and they flew in through the window and dirtied the house.

Rabbi Chanina ben Dosa decided to sell all of the hens and the chicks, and use the money to buy goats.

"The goats will go out to the forest to eat," he thought, "and I won't have to feed them." Each morning the goats went outdoors to eat weeds in the forest, and every evening they returned to their shed.

A few years later, the man who had left the chickens at Rabbi Chanina's house was passing through the town. When he walked by Rabbi Chanina's house, he remembered the place, and he said to a friend who was with him, "I once left some chickens here for a short while, but then I forgot where I had left them and I never found them again."

Rabbi Chanina ben Dosa overheard their conversation. He looked out the window and asked the man, "Can you prove that the hens were yours? Do you remember the color of their feathers? Do you know what kind of string you had tied around their feet?"

"Oh, yes," replied the man. "The hens were brown and their feet were tied with a red cord."

Rabbi Chanina was satisfied. He brought the man to the barn and showed him the goats.

"These goats belong to you," he said. "I bought them with the money I got from selling the chickens you left at my doorstep."

The man was very surprised and very pleased. He thanked Rabbi Chanina ben Dosa warmly and returned home with his goats.

Source: Talmud Bavli, Ta'anith 25

The cloth merchant

av Safra was a very wise man. For a few hours each day, he sold cloth in his store so that he could earn a little money for food, but most of the day he studied the Torah and prayed.

One day some customers came to his store and asked, "Do you have any good cloth to sell us?"

"Yes," said Rav Safra, showing them the material.

The customers liked the cloth. "How much does it cost?" they asked.

"Ten coins," replied Rav Safra.

"Ten coins?! That's much too expensive!" they complained. "We'll pay you five coins."

Rav Safra shook his head. "No, I cannot sell this fine cloth for only five coins," he said.

The people left the store. But later that night they thought, "We really should have bought that cloth. It was worth the ten coins that Rav Safra asked for it. Tomorrow morning we will go back and buy it."

Rav Safra was also thinking. "I am sorry that I

The customers liked the cloth.
"How much does it cost?"

didn't sell the cloth for five coins. True, it's worth more, but I need the money badly! If they return tomorrow, I will sell it for five coins."

The following morning the customers came to Rav Safra and said, "Greetings. We have come back for the cloth that we wanted to buy last night."

But just then, Rav Safra was saying the *Shema,* and he couldn't speak to the customers. When he finished his *tefilloth* (prayers), the customers repeated their offer.

"We have returned to buy the cloth. We will pay you ten coins for it," they said.

"No," answered Rav Safra. "I made up my mind to sell it to you for five coins, and I will not accept more money."

The customers were impressed by his honesty. "Rav Safra is truly a righteous man," they said.

Source: She'iltoth de Rabbi Achai Ga'on

Love for our fellow man

Aharon
the peace-maker

haron Hakohen (Aaron the Priest), the brother of Moshe, was beloved by all the people of Israel. He never lost his temper and he never scolded anyone. Even when he knew that someone had done something wrong, he never said, "Wicked man, what an evil thing you have done!" He would just greet him politely, as if nothing had happened. The man would walk away feeling very ashamed, and would ask himself, "How can I face the friendly Aharon? If he only knew what wicked things I have done, he certainly wouldn't say hello to me. He wouldn't want to speak to me at all. He probably wouldn't even look at me!" The next time the man was tempted to do something bad, he would think of Aharon and he would stop.

Sometimes people quarreled and were angry and refused to speak to each other. What did Aharon do?

He sat down with the first man and said to him, "Do you know that I saw your friend, the one with whom you quarreled? He is very sorry that he

Love for our fellow man

made you angry. He feels so bad! He says it's all his fault that you're angry, and he's very ashamed of himself."

Aharon kept telling these things to the first man until he felt that the man was no longer angry at his friend.

Then he went to the second man and said, "I was just visiting your friend. He is very upset that you are angry at him. He says it's all his fault, and he is very ashamed of himself. He wishes you were his friend again!" Aharon spoke to the second man until he, too, was willing to make up. When the two men met the next day, they would smile and shake hands, and they became good friends again.

This is how Aharon made peace among the Jewish people. And for this, the people loved him.

Sources: Avoth de Rabbi Nathan, chapter 12
         Yalkut Shimoni, Chukkath

The patience of Hillel

illel came from the family of David Hamelech (King David), and he was himself the *nasi*, the leader of the Jews in Israel.

No one was wiser or more respected than he. Great rabbis came to speak to him and students came to study with him, but Hillel was not proud. Never once did he become impatient or angry. He spoke kindly and lovingly to every man.

Once, two men were talking about the *nasi*. One of them said, "Hillel the Elder does not get angry at anyone or anything."

The other man laughed and said, "I will make him so angry that he will scold me."

"I don't believe it's possible," said the first. "I am ready to make a bet with you. If you really make Hillel angry, I will pay you four hundred coins of silver."

His friend laughed again and said, "The money is mine already! I know just how to make him angry."

It was Erev Shabbath. Hillel was busy preparing for the Shabbath. He was bathing and washing his hair when he heard someone calling in a shrill voice, "Which of these houses belongs to Hillel? Where does he live? Which house is his?"

Someone else might certainly have become angry at the man shouting rudely, as if he didn't know where the famous Hillel lived. And to come looking for him on Erev Shabbath when everyone was so busy!

But Hillel wasn't angry. "Perhaps he has an important question to ask and he needs an immediate answer," he thought.

Hillel hurriedly dressed and went outside.

"What do you want, my son?" he asked quietly.

"I have a question to ask," the man said.

"Ask your question, my son," answered Hillel.

"Why do the Babylonians have egg-shaped heads?" he asked.

The man did not really expect an answer to such a silly question. He only wanted to make Hillel angry by bothering him on Erev Shabbath when he was so busy.

But Hillel answered him gently. "My son," he said, "you have asked a very important question. The reason the Babylonians have egg-shaped heads is that the midwives in Babylonia don't know how to handle newborn babies."

The man went away and waited long enough

for Hillel to begin his Shabbath preparations again. Then he returned to Hillel's house and shouted, "Which of these houses belongs to Hillel? Where does he live?"

But Hillel did not get angry this time either. He dressed in a hurry and once again greeted the man.

"What is it you want, my son?" he asked.

"I have a question," said the man, in a gruff voice.

"Ask your question, my son."

Again, the man asked a very silly-sounding question. "Why do the people of Tadmur have narrow, half-closed eyes?"

"You have asked a good question," said Hillel. "The reason is that the city of Tadmur is in the desert, and the wind blows sand in the eyes of the desert dwellers. Therefore, *Hashem,* in His pity, made their eyes narrow and half-closed so that the sand would not hurt their eyes."

The man left, waited a while, and returned again, shouting and calling, "Where is Hillel? Where is his house?"

Hillel got dressed for a third time, went out and asked patiently, "My son, what do you want?"

"I have a question for you!" he said.

"Ask, my son, ask the question," said Hillel kindly.

"Why do the people of Africa have wide feet?"

*"I have many questions to ask, but I am afraid
you will be angry at me."*

But this time, too, Hillel answered carefully and quietly. "My son, you have asked a very interesting question. The reason is that many people of Africa live where it is very muddy, and *Hashem* made their feet wide so that they would not sink so easily into the mud and the swamps."

The man saw that he was not making Hillel angry, so he thought, "I will speak to him disrespectfully and then he'll surely get angry, and I will be able to collect the money on my bet."

So he said, "I have many questions to ask, but I am afraid that you will be angry at me."

Hillel sat down and invited the man to sit down with him. He spoke calmly, without hurrying to finish. "Ask all the questions you want and I will try to answer them."

"Are you the same Hillel who is known as the *nasi* of Israel?" the man asked.

"Yes," answered Hillel.

"If you are he, then I pray that there won't be many more people like you in Israel!" said the man bitterly.

"But why not?" asked Hillel, still quiet and calm.

Angrily, the man replied, "Because of you, I lost four hundred silver coins! My friend promised me this sum if I could make you angry, but you didn't once lose your temper!"

"In the future, do not bet on such wicked

things," Hillel replied. "It is better to lose twice four hundred coins than to make Hillel angry."

The man left. He had learned his lesson and was ashamed of his behavior.

Source: Talmud Bavli, Shabbath 30-31

Hillel and the heathen

In the time of the *beith hamikdash*, there were two great rabbis in Yerushalayim—Shammai and Hillel. Shammai was very strict and had little patience with people who did not act properly. But Hillel was a very patient man. He was never angry.

Once, a heathen (non-Jew) came to Shammai and said, "I want to become a Jew, but I have one condition. You must teach me the whole Torah while I stand on one foot!"

When Shammai heard this, he became angry. How could one learn the entire Torah while standing on one foot?! Even a whole lifetime of study is not enough for a man to learn the entire Torah!

Shammai was holding a long measuring stick. He took the stick, pushed the heathen out of the house, and chased him away.

Then the heathen went to Hillel. "I want to be a Jew," he said, "but on the condition that you teach me the whole Torah while I stand on one foot!"

105

"Fine," Hillel replied patiently. "I will do as you say."

The heathen stood on one foot and Hillel taught him, "Whatever is hateful to you, do not do unto your fellow man. This is the message of the Torah. Now go and learn all the laws so that you will know exactly what to do and what not to do."

The heathen listened to Hillel and did as he was told. He studied the Torah and eventually became a good Jew.

Source: Talmud Bavli, Shabbath 31

7

Deeds of lovingkindness

Abba Yudan

In the city of Antioch there lived a good man who was very generous and charitable. He gave much of his money to the poor, and he supported the wise men who sat and studied Torah night and day. In addition, he always gave his *tzedakah* willingly and generously. His name was Abba Yudan.

For a while, Abba Yudan prospered. But then bad fortune befell him. He lost all of his money and was forced to sell his fields in order to buy food for his wife and children. Finally, out of the many fields he had owned, he had only one left.

One day, three great Sages—Rabbi Eliezer, Rabbi Yehoshua and Rabbi Akiva—arrived in the city to collect money for poor scholars. When Abba Yudan saw them, he was very upset. He remembered how he had always given so much *tzedakah,* and now he had nothing to give. He came home feeling very unhappy. His wife, seeing his sad face, said, "What is the matter with you? Are you sick? Why do you look so unhappy?"

"Our rabbis have come to collect money for charity and we have nothing to give," Abba Yudan replied.

Abba Yudan's wife was even more righteous than her husband. She thought for a while and said, "We still have one field left. Go and sell half of it, and give the money to the Sages."

Abba Yudan took her advice, sold half of his field and gave the money he had received to the Sages. In their great wisdom, the rabbis understood what Abba Yudan had done.

What did they do in turn? They recorded his contribution at the head of their list, even though others had given more than he, and they prayed to *Hashem* that He help Abba Yudan and bless him as a reward for his good deeds. They said, "May the Lord fill all your needs. May it be His will that all you have given to charity be returned to you." Then they gave the money they had collected to the poor and needy.

One day Abba Yudan went to plow the remaining half of his field. His cow, the only one he had left, was pulling the plow. Suddenly a large hole appeared in the field. The cow stumbled into the hole and broke her leg.

What a misfortune for Abba Yudan! How would he plow his field now that his cow was hurt? But Abba Yudan did not complain. He bent over to help the cow, when he saw something glittering in the dirt. He looked more closely, and to his amazement, a box full of gold was lying at the bottom of the hole!

Abba Yudan thanked *Hashem* and said, "The Holy One, blessed be He, does everything for the best. My cow broke her leg so that I would find this treasure. It was all done for my good."

From then on, Abba Yudan had no more worries. With his newly found gold, he bought back his fields and beautiful house, and he purchased cows, goats, lambs, camels, and oxen.

After a while, the rabbis came back to the city and asked the people about Abba Yudan. "Abba Yudan?" the people said. "Do you mean the man with all the servants? The one with houses and fields, cows and camels, goats and sheep? He has become a very wealthy and important man, well respected in the community!"

When Abba Yudan heard of the rabbis' arrival, he gave them a warm welcome and invited them to his home. The Sages asked him, "What are you doing these days, Abba Yudan? How are you?"

Abba Yudan replied, "The Holy One, blessed be He, answered your prayers on my behalf. He has given me many blessings." Then he told them all that had happened to him. The rabbis honored him with their company and rejoiced with him over the blessings *Hashem* had sent.

Abba Yudan was richly rewarded because even

Deeds of lovingkindness

in the days when he was poor, he performed the *mitzvah* of *tzedakah* willingly and generously. And now he was able to give more *tzedakah* than ever before.

Source: Midrash Vayikra Rabbah, chapter 5

The clear decision

Abba Tachna was a pious man who loved *Hashem* and observed the *mitzvoth* of the Torah. All week long he worked outside the city, and on Erev Shabbath he would come home, bringing a bundle of food and clothes for his family. His load was heavy, but Abba Tachna walked quickly in order to be home in time for Shabbath.

As he walked, Abba Tachna was busy thinking. "How happy my wife and children will be with all the good things I am bringing! They are probably waiting anxiously for me by now." And so, Abba Tachna walked even faster.

Suddenly he saw a man lying in the middle of the road, crying and groaning. Abba Tachna came closer to see what had happened. The man was covered with bruises from head to foot. He was in such pain that he couldn't move.

In a feeble voice, the sick man begged Abba Tachna, "Please help me, Rabbi. Have pity on me and take me with you. I am too sick to move. If I remain here alone, I will die of pain and hunger."

Abba Tachna thought, "What shall I do? I can't carry both the man and the bundle. If I bring the sick man home, my bundle might be stolen before I can come back to take it. Or perhaps I might not be able to get home in time for Shabbath. And, how will my family live without the supplies I am bringing home? Everything I own is in my bundle. I have nothing else. But if I bring the bundle home first, and then come back for the sick man, he might die, God forbid, before I get here."

But Abba Tachna did not think for long. The decision was clear. "First, I will see to it that the man gets home," he decided, "and then I will worry about my bundle."

He put down the bundle, picked up the man, and walked slowly and carefully so as not to hurt him. With much trouble, he finally reached the sick man's house and put him to bed. Then he hurried back to the road to take his bundle. Fortunately, it was still there.

Abba Tachna picked up his load and hurried home towards the city. In the meantime, the sun had set and the townspeople were walking to the *beith knesseth* dressed in their Shabbath clothes and carrying their *siddurim*. And there was Abba Tachna still in his work clothes, with a big bundle on his shoulders.

The townspeople were very surprised and said

to one another, "Could this be the pious Abba Tachna who is so careful about observing the *mitzvoth*? Look, he's desecrating the Shabbath!"

Abba Tachna himself was terribly worried. "Have I really violated Shabbath?" he asked himself.

The Holy One, blessed be He, saw how troubled this good man was, and He returned the sun to the sky. When the people saw that the sun had not yet set, they knew that the Shabbath had not yet begun.

Abba Tachna hurried home, bathed, got dressed in honor of Shabbath, and went to the *beith knesseth*. He was happy that *Hashem* had given him the chance to do two *mitzvoth*—saving a sick man and bringing his bundle of supplies home to his family without desecrating the Shabbath.

Source: Midrash Koheleth Rabbah, chapter 9

The guardian
of a treasure

poor laborer once worked for a land-
owner. Every day he went out to plow
the fields and do all the work that
needed to be done. Every evening he
received his wages and went to buy food for his
wife and children. Although he worked long and
hard, he earned barely enough to support his
family. But the man did not complain and was
always happy with whatever he had.

One day, as he was hard at work in the field,
Eliyahu Hanavi (the Prophet Elijah) appeared. He
was dressed as an Arab. Eliyahu greeted the poor
man, and the man returned his greeting. Then
Eliyahu said, *"Hashem* knows that you are a poor,
hard-working man. He wants to give you six years
of riches, and with your new wealth, you will be
able to buy anything you desire. When do you
want your six years of wealth—now or later?"

The man did not believe the stranger's promises of wealth. "Please don't bother me," he replied. "I have to get my work done and I have no
money to give you, so go in peace!"

*Elijah the Prophet appeared to him
dressed as an Arab.*

Deeds of lovingkindness

Eliyahu Hanavi went away, but the next day, as the poor man was plowing the fields, he came back again. "*Hashem* wants to give you six years of riches and comfort. When do you want those years to come?"

The poor man was annoyed at being disturbed again, and he said impatiently, "I don't believe what you are saying. Please, don't bother me. Go away."

But the following day, when Eliyahu Hanavi returned for a third time, the man thought that perhaps the stranger was really telling the truth. So he said, "Wait here, and I'll go ask my wife."

The man went home and told his wife, "For three days, a man dressed as an Arab has come to me and told me that *Hashem* wants to give me six years of wealth. He wants to know whether I would like the rich years now or later. What shall I tell him?"

His wife replied, "Ask for the good years to start now."

The man returned to the field where Eliyahu was waiting for him. He said, "We would like to have the good years now rather than later."

"Good," said Eliyahu Hanavi with satisfaction. "Return home and you will find that *Hashem* has blessed you."

Meanwhile, the man's children had been playing in the sand and had found a box full of money. "Mother," they called excitedly, "come see what we have found!"

The mother came and saw that there was enough money in the box to support the family for several years. When the father returned home and heard about the new-found treasure, he was very happy. He praised *Hashem* for all His goodness. Then he turned to his wife and asked, "What shall we do with all of this money?"

His wife answered wisely, "We will not buy fancy things, nor will we eat expensive foods. We will use the money only for plain food and clothes we really need. The rest of the money will be for *tzedakah* and deeds of *chessed*."

The woman sent her son to buy a notebook and a pen and every day she would say to him, "Please write down the amount of money we gave to *tzedakah* today." The boy did as his mother told him.

Six years later, Eliyahu Hanavi came back. "The time has come for you to return everything *Hashem* has given you," he said.

"First let me go home and tell my wife," said the man.

"The old man has come to take back the money," he told his wife.

"Show him our notebook with the account of the money and how we have spent it," she replied. "Tell him, 'If there are people who will use the money in a better way than we have used it, then give the money to them!' "

Hashem knew everything the man and his wife had done with the money. He had seen them cure the sick, give food to the hungry and buy clothes for the poor. Therefore, He told Eliyahu Hanavi not to take away their wealth. On the contrary! He commanded him to increase their fortunes so that they could live in peace and do good deeds for the rest of their lives.

Source: Midrash Yalkut Shimoni, 427

Hillel's wife

illel was so poor in his early days that he didn't even have enough bread to eat. Only later in life, when he became the *nasi* (leader of Israel), was he well-to-do. But even then he lived simply, and his wife used to prepare their meals herself.

An important guest once came to visit the elderly Hillel. Hillel wanted to honor his visitor with a good meal, so he went to his wife and said, "Please prepare a special meal for our guest."

Hillel's wife hurried to the kitchen and kneaded dough to bake bread, for in those days there were no bakeries and every woman baked her own bread. She made a fire in the oven and put in the dough. Then she prepared the meat with vegetables and pudding. Finally everything was finished and tastefully prepared.

The wife was about to bring the bread and the other food to Hillel and his guest, when she heard a knock at the door. She opened the door, and there, standing in the doorway, was a young man looking sad and forlorn.

121 🌺

"Welcome. May I help you?" she asked.

The man answered, "Today is my wedding day. The bride and the wedding guests are assembled and waiting. But I haven't earned any money for a long time, and my bride is poor too. We have no money to prepare the feast for the wedding guests, and I am ashamed to come to the wedding ceremony empty-handed."

Hillel's wife took the bread and all the good food she had prepared for their guest, and she gave them to the man who took them gratefully. He brought the meal to the guests who had come to his wedding, and they all enjoyed a festive dinner.

What did Hillel's wife do then?

She started all the preparations anew. She kneaded the dough and baked another batch of bread and cooked more meat.

All this time, Hillel and his visitor sat together, studying Torah. It was getting late and the visitor was hungry. Hillel was surprised that his wife had not yet brought the meal, but he did not want to call her. He knew that she was a good woman, and whatever she did was always good.

At last she came in, set the table, and brought the meal.

"What took you so long, my dear?" Hillel asked her.

His wife told him the story. "A poor man came to the house and said that today was his wedding

The wife of Hillel took the bread and all the tasty delicacies and gave them to the man.

day, but he had no food to serve the wedding guests. So I gave him the food I had made and I prepared your meal all over again."

Hillel praised his wife and said, "Dearest wife, everything you did was done for the sake of Heaven. *Hashem* will surely be happy with your deeds of kindness."

Source: Talmud Bavli, Derech Eretz, chapter 6

The secret gift

There was a great rabbi in Babylonia whose name was Mar Ukva. All day long Mar Ukva was occupied with the study of Torah and with doing *mitzvoth*. He gave many gifts to the poor, and in order not to embarrass them, he did not send the money through others, but distributed the gifts himself. But he did not give them the money directly.

"If the poor do not know who their benefactor is," thought the righteous Mar Ukva, "they will give thanks to *Hashem* alone."

So when he had money to deliver, he came to the house of the poor, threw the money in through an opening in the door, and quickly went away. The poor man would find the money but he would not find the person who had put it there.

Once it happened that Mar Ukva remained in the *beith midrash* later than usual. His wife came to see why he was so late coming home.

Mar Ukva had not yet given his *tzedakah* that day. So after he finished his studies, he took his wife with him as he went to the house of a poor man.

The poor man was waiting at home. He wanted to see who it was who left *tzedakah* at his door day after day. The man leaned out the window and saw Mar Ukva and his wife.

"These must be the people who have been helping me!" he thought and went out to thank them for their kindness.

But when Mar Ukva and his wife saw him, they hurried away as fast as they could. They did not want to be recognized. Looking for a place to hide, they found a large, open oven in a yard nearby. The fire was out, so they hid inside. But the floor of the oven was still very hot, and Mar Ukva's feet were painfully burned by the hot bricks.

"Put your feet on mine," said his wife. "My feet are not burned."

Why didn't the hot bricks burn her feet as well as her husband's? Because every day Mar Ukva's wife gave food, rather than money, to the poor. They were able to sit down in her house and eat their fill without waiting and working — without going to the store, cooking, and preparing. Therefore, the Holy One, blessed be He, performed a miracle for her as a reward for her work and her kindness.

Mar Ukva and his wife waited in the oven until the poor man stopped looking for them. Then they hurriedly left the money at his door and returned home.

Why did they stay in the hot oven? Because they did not want to embarrass the man for taking charity from other people. And they wanted him to understand that all help comes from *Hashem*. Although the Holy One, blessed be He, sends His help through messengers, it is not important to know who these messengers are.

Source: Talmud Bavli, Kethuvoth 67b

How to give tzedakah

Once there was a lonely boy who had no one to help him or care for him — neither father nor mother, aunts nor uncles, nor any other relatives.

The boy was wandering through the streets, hungry and unhappy, when a kind man found him and took him home. He fed the boy and gave him nice clothes to wear and a clean bed in which to sleep.

The boy remained with the man, went to school and studied. When he grew up, he learned a trade, so that he would be able to earn a living for himself.

The kind man gave him a house and money to open a workshop. Soon the young man was quite rich.

But the man who had been so kind to him suddenly lost his money and became quite poor. "I will go to the young man whom I took care of all these years, and I will ask him for some money," he thought. "He will surely want to help me."

He went to the young man and was warmly

welcomed. They had a long, friendly conversation. They spoke about many things. The older man was ashamed to ask for money, but finally, in a soft voice so that no one else should hear, he said, "I have come to ask a favor — a loan. I have lost all of my money, and I have nothing left to support myself with."

The young man felt very bad that this kind man, who had done him so many favors and had given so much money to the poor, must now ask for money for himself.

He tried to comfort his friend while to himself he thought, "I wonder how I can help him without embarrassing him?" Then he had an idea. "I will give him a gift without letting him know that it's from me."

He told the man, "*Hashem* will surely help you because of your good deeds, and you will be as prosperous as before."

But he did not give the poor man any money. He merely said, "It is hard for me to give you money right now. But I will see...I will try...we will talk some more about this matter."

The man took leave of his friend and went home.

As soon as he left, the young man called one of his servants and instructed him to put on patched and torn clothes. Then he gave him an expensive pearl and sent him to the home of the good man.

"Do you want to buy a beautiful pearl?"

When the man answered the door, the servant showed him the precious jewel.

"Do you want to buy a beautiful pearl?" he asked.

"How much does it cost?" asked the man.

"One dinar," the servant replied.

"That is very cheap!" thought the man. "I only have one dinar, but it's surely worth spending it on a pearl. I should be able to sell the pearl at a good profit." So he bought the pearl and paid for it with his only coin.

A few days later the young man sent out another servant, dressed in beautiful clothes and with a great deal of money, and told him just what to do. The servant, looking like a rich man, went to the poor man's home and said, "I have heard that you sell pearls. I need one beautiful pearl. Do you have one for sale?"

The man took out the pearl he had bought a few days earlier. "This is exactly what I want!" exclaimed the servant. "Will you sell it for a thousand dinar?"

The man readily agreed to sell the jewel, and the servant returned the pearl to his master.

The poor man thus received a large sum of money, without knowing that it was really a gift from the young man. He went happily to the young man and said, "You needn't worry about helping me anymore. *Baruch Hashem* —thank God—I was able to make a good sale and I was left with a fine profit."

Both men were very pleased. The good man was happy he didn't need charity, and the young man was happy to have given *tzedakah* without embarrassing the person who received it.

Source: Me'il Tzedakah

Guarding one's tongue

Speaking good and evil

Rabban Shimon ben Gamliel was one of the heads of the *Sanhedrin*, the supreme court in Israel. He was the grandson of Hillel and, like his grandfather, he was a wise man and a great scholar.

Many people learned Torah from him including his servant, Tovi, who was always in his master's company.

One day Rabbi Shimon called Tovi and said, "Go to the market and buy something good to eat."

Tovi went to the butcher and bought the tongue of a cow. "Here," he said when he came home, "I have brought you a delicacy."

"Fine!" said Rabbi Shimon. "And now go and buy me something bad to eat."

Tovi was surprised, but he went back to the market just as his master had ordered. On the way there he thought, "Why did Rabbi Shimon tell me to buy bad food for him? Why does he need bad food? He must want to teach me and his other students something important. But what could it be?"

Tovi thought for a while, and suddenly he understood. When he reached the market, he went back into the butcher shop and bought another tongue! Then he returned to Rabbi Shimon with the second tongue.

"Tell me, Tovi," said Rabbi Shimon. "What have you done? When I asked you to buy me something good to eat, you bought me a tongue. And when I asked you to buy me something bad to eat, you bought a tongue again. Is the tongue both good and bad?"

"Yes, it is," answered Tovi. "When the tongue is good, there is nothing better, and when it is bad, there is nothing worse. When people speak the words of the Torah or pray," continued Tovi, "and when they speak kind and wise words to each other, the tongue is very good. But when people speak harshly and insult or hurt others, the tongue is very bad."

Rabbi Shimon ben Gamliel was happy that Tovi had understood the lesson he was meant to learn. He explained the story to all of his students so that they, too, would guard their tongues against speaking evil, and would always speak gently and kindly to each other.

Source: Midrash Vayikra Rabbah, chapter 33

Soft tongues
and hard tongues

abbi Yehudah, who was known as "Rabbi" for short by his many students, wanted his pupils to remember to speak gently and carefully to their fellow men.

What did he do?

He invited all his pupils to a feast and ordered two kinds of food. He asked to be served both well-cooked tongues which were soft and tender, and half-cooked tongues which were half-raw and tough.

Rabbi himself came to the feast. "Please eat, my sons," he said to his pupils. "Choose any of the tongues you want."

None of the students wanted to eat the hard tongues. They all chose the tasty, tender ones.

Rabbi saw this and said with satisfaction, "Look carefully, my sons, so that you may understand what you are doing. All of you have left the hard tongues, and you have chosen to eat the soft ones instead."

Then he continued, "Do the same when you

Guarding one's tongue

speak. Do not speak with a hard tongue, in harsh and angry tones. Speak to each other with a soft tongue, using gentle and kind words.''

Source: Midrash Vayikra Rabbah, chapter 33

The best medicine

ot far from the city of Zippori, there lived a salesman who used to sell spices and medicines of all kinds. Every day he went with his merchandise from city to city and from street to street. He came to the marketplace and to the courtyards and called out in a loud voice, "Whoever wants to live long, come buy this potion of life! Whoever wants a wonderful medicine, come to me!"

Everywhere, people hearing the chant, looked out the windows and came running to the salesman. For who would not want to buy a wonderful cure that promises long life?

In one city, there lived a teacher named Rabbi Yannai. Rabbi Yannai was at home studying the Torah, when suddenly he heard a voice outside calling, "Come and buy a wonderful cure—a medicine for long life!"

Rabbi Yannai looked out the window and saw the salesman surrounded by many customers.

"What is this medicine the man is prescrib-

*"Come and buy a wonderful cure
a medicine for long life."*

ing?" thought Rabbi Yannai. "I must find out if he is telling the truth!"

He called the salesman, "Hear, my good man! Please come up and sell me some of your wonderful medicine."

When the salesman saw the rabbi, he was embarrassed. "Rabbi," he said, "you, and people like you who study the Torah and fulfill the *mitzvoth*, don't need this medicine."

"Just the same, please come up and show me," said Rabbi Yannai.

The salesman did not want to come at first, but Rabbi Yannai persisted until he finally agreed.

"Now," said Rabbi Yannai, "where is this wonderful medicine?"

The salesman opened his bag and took out a *Sefer Tehillim* in which we find the songs and *tefilloth* of David Hamelech (King David), may he rest in peace. The salesman gave the book to the rabbi.

"Is this the medicine for long life?"

The salesman opened the book and pointed to the sentence, "Who is the man who wants life? Guard your tongue from speaking evil!" Then he said, "I teach this sentence to all the people who come to buy."

"You are right," said Rabbi Yannai. "This is indeed the potion of life! Only now do I fully understand this beautiful sentence. David Ha-

Guarding one's tongue

melech warned us to guard our tongue from saying unkind things about other people. If we do so, *Hashem* will grant us long life in *gan eden*. And Shlomoh Hamelech, who was the wisest of all men, said, 'One who guards his mouth and tongue guards his soul from trouble!' That is really a wonderful medicine. May many people buy it. Go in peace, my good man!'"

Rabbi Yannai thanked the salesman and sent him on his way.

Source: Midrash Vayikra Rabbah, chapter 16

Love for the Torah and for those who study it

Studying Torah in poverty

efore Hillel became the *nasi* (the leader of Israel) he was very poor. But as long as he had enough money to feed his family and to study in the *beith midrash* where the great teachers, Shemaya and Avtalyon, taught the Torah, he was happy.

Hillel worked very hard, but earned very little. Every day he divided his money into two parts. Half went to buy bread for himself and his family, and half went to the watchman at the *beith midrash*.

But on one Friday — Erev Shabbath — Hillel could not find any work and, therefore, did not earn any money. He was unhappy that he had no money to buy Shabbath candles, wine for *kiddush*, or flour for *challah*. But he was even more unhappy that he had no money to enter the *beith midrash*.

Hillel stood outside the *beith midrash* and thought, "The rabbis and their pupils are sitting inside learning the words of the Torah, while I am outside, unable to enter. How I wish I could hear what they are saying!"

It was the month of Teveth, in the middle of winter, and it was very cold outside. Inside the *beith midrash*, it was warm and pleasant. A fire was blazing in the big oven, and the smoke came out of the chimney on the roof. But Hillel wasn't interested in the warm oven. He wanted the warmth of the Torah!

Then he remembered that there was a window on the roof to let in light. He would be able to hear from there! He climbed up on the roof and bent over the window. He heard the words of Shemaya and Avtalyon and was even able to see them sitting near the warm oven. All day long Hillel lay on the roof listening. He did not feel the cold at all — so great was his love of Torah.

When night came, everything froze. Hillel was stiff from the bitter cold. He lay down near the chimney to keep warm, for he had no strength to get up. Snow started falling, slowly covering him from head to toe. But Hillel did not feel anything; he had fainted from weakness and cold.

In the *beith midrash*, the people welcomed the Shabbath, prayed and went home. At home, they made *kiddush* on the wine and ate their Shabbath meal. Then they returned to the *beith midrash* and continued learning Torah all night long. They loved the Torah so much that they did not want to go home to sleep. So they sat there studying until the morning.

At the break of dawn, when it was beginning to get light outside, Shemaya said to Avtalyon, "Avtalyon, my brother, why isn't there any daylight in the room? It is morning already, but inside it is still dark. Perhaps it is a cloudy day, and the sun is not visible."

They glanced up towards the skylight to see if there were clouds in the sky, and what did they see? A man stretched out on the roof!

The students went up to the roof at once. They dug in the snow and uncovered the person who was lying there. They looked at him and saw their friend Hillel!

The students quickly brought him down to the *beith midrash*. They washed him and rubbed him with snow so that he would wake up. Even though it was the Shabbath, they washed him and rubbed him with oil. Then they sat him in front of the fire until he was warm and began to breathe.

"We may violate the Shabbath in order to save a life," said Shemaya and Avtalyon, "especially for a man like Hillel, who was ready to give up his own life in order to study the Torah."

Hillel recovered. Day after day, he studied and learned with his teachers until he became a Sage, a teacher and a leader for all of Israel.

Source: Talmud Bavli, Yoma 35

Wealth and Torah

There was once a man in Eretz Yisrael by the name of Charsom. He was a very rich man. He owned a thousand towns and farms and all the houses on them, and the people who lived on his farms were obligated to work for him.

He also had a thousand ships that sailed to faraway places and brought back whatever he desired — gold and precious stones, fragrant spices and fine silk for clothing. Charsom sold these things and became even richer.

Charsom had only one son, Elazar. When the father grew old and died, Elazar inherited all his wealth, including the towns and farms and the ships.

But Elazar did not like all this wealth. He never went to see the towns he owned nor did he care about his ships. Elazar loved the Torah, and all he wanted was to study it.

But the merchants who came to buy and sell were always interrupting him; servants were constantly calling to ask what he wished to eat and drink; and all sorts of people came to honor the rich young man.

What did Elazar do? He put on the simple clothes of a poor man. He took a sack full of flour to bake bread when he was hungry, and he quietly left his house. He walked a long time until he came to another city, where he could study the Torah.

He did not remain long in this city either, because he was afraid that people would recognize him and begin to bother him. And so he wandered from city to city, and from state to state. In each city he went to the rabbi or the *yeshivah*, where he sat and studied with great joy.

After several years, he himself became a rabbi and was known as Rabbi Elazar ben Charsom. But even then, he continued to wander from place to place to learn more Torah.

Once while he was walking on the road, he met some of his servants. They did not recognize him, for he looked like a poor man. His clothes were old, and he carried a sack of food on his back. "Stop!" his servants called to him. "Why are you walking down the road instead of working? We saw you leave the town which belongs to our master, Rabbi Elazar ben Charsom. You must be a servant, and you are supposed to be working now. Come back with us at once and do your job!"

Rabbi Elazar did not want to tell them that *he* was the master, and so he said, "Please let me continue on my way in peace, for I want to study the Torah."

"You lazy good-for-nothing!" shouted the servants. "We will not let you go! You are supposed to be working for Rabbi Elazar!"

Rabbi Elazar begged them to set him free, but they would not listen. Since he did not want to tell them who he was, he took the money he had brought along for traveling expenses and gave it to them. "Take my money and let me go," he said.

The servants were happy to take the money, and Rabbi Elazar continued on his way, grateful to be left alone. The money was not at all important to him. His only desire was to spend his time in the study of the Torah.

Source: Talmud Bavli, Yoma 35

"Take my money and let me go."

Eliezer ben Hyrcanus

abbi Eliezer ben Hyrcanus was one of the greatest and most important of our Sages, may their memory be for a blessing. But when he was young, he did not study the Torah at all. He did not even know how to pray or say the *Shema* or the *Birkath Hamazon.* He was a strong, tall young man who worked the soil, and every day he went out with his brothers to plow his father's fields.

His brothers worked in the valley where the land was straight and clear of stones, while Eliezer plowed on the hill, where the soil was hard and rocky. One day, he sat in the field and began to cry.

"Why are you crying?" his father asked. "Is it because your brothers have easier work while you have to plow this rocky soil? Don't cry! You may go and plow in the valley with your brothers."

Eliezer went down to plow in the valley, but still he continued to cry. "Why are you crying now?" his father asked. "Are you sorry that I sent you to the valley to plow?"

"No," answered Eliezer.

"Then why are you crying? What is the matter?"

"I want to study Torah," replied Eliezer. "If I have enough strength to plow hard, rocky soil, I have enough strength to study the Torah, too."

His father laughed. "You want to study the Torah! A fellow as big as you will now start to study?" he said. "You are old enough to marry. When you have children of your own, you will take *them* to school to study!"

But Eliezer was not convinced. "I will go to Yerushalayim, and I will study with the great teacher Rabbi Yochanan ben Zakkai," he said.

His father became angry. "Go and finish plowing!" he shouted.

"Let my son work good and hard, and he will soon forget all about studying Torah," thought Hyrcanus.

Eliezer rose early the following morning. When he finished his work in the field, he did not go home to eat. Instead he started out on foot to Yerushalayim. He took no supplies with him, and he had no money to buy food. When he became very hungry, he took a mouthful of soil and chewed it so that he wouldn't feel his hunger.

At last he came to Yerushalayim. He went straight to the *beith midrash* where Rabbi Yochanan ben Zakkai was teaching. Eliezer sat quietly on the side. He listened carefully, but he could not understand a word, for until now he had never studied anything. So he sat on the side and cried.

Rabbi Yochanan saw him. "Why are you crying, my son?" he asked the strange young man.

"Because I want to study and understand the Torah, just as your other students do," answered Eliezer.

Rabbi Yochanan looked at him and saw that he was already a young man, not a child just starting to learn.

"What have you learned until now?" he asked.

"Nothing," answered Eliezer.

"Then I will teach you the *Shema*, *Birkath Hamazon*, and the other prayers," said Rabbi Yochanan.

Rabbi Yochanan began to teach and Eliezer began to learn. Rabbi Yochanan taught him more and more, while Eliezer reviewed and reviewed until he knew everything perfectly.

Eliezer loved his learning so much, that he almost forgot he was hungry. And when he remembered, he had nothing to eat. So he chewed on pieces of soil. Eight days passed. When Rabbi Yochanan smelled an unpleasant odor coming from his pupil's mouth, he realized that Eliezer, this wonderful pupil, had probably not eaten for a long time.

"Eliezer, have you eaten today?" he asked.

Eliezer was ashamed to say that he had not eaten for eight days, so he remained silent.

Rabbi Yochanan ben Zakkai told two of his *talmidim* to go to the house where Eliezer was staying and to find out if he had eaten there. The students went to the house and asked the landlady, "Does our friend Eliezer live here?"

"Yes," answered the woman.

"Has he been taking his meals with you?" they asked.

"No," she said. "We thought he's eating at the home of Rabbi Yochanan ben Zakkai." Then she added, "I saw him take out something from his bag and chew on it. Perhaps he has food in the bag."

They opened Eliezer's bag and found clods of dirt.

The students went back to Rabbi Yochanan and told him the story. Rabbi Yochanan immediately called Eliezer. "Eliezer, my son," he said, "just as an unpleasant odor came forth from your lips when you suffered for the Torah, one day your good name will be on the lips of all Jews when you become a *talmid chacham.*

"And from this day on," he added, "you will eat at my table."

Eliezer stayed with Rabbi Yochanan ben Zakkai and studied the Torah for many years, until he became a wise and learned man.

One day, Rabbi Yochanan made a big feast. He

invited all the rabbis and wise men and all of the important and respected people in Yerushalayim. They sat at a long table and Rabbi Yochanan led a discussion in matters of Torah.

Suddenly a stranger appeared among the guests, a man who had not been invited. It was Abba Hyrcanus, the father of Rabbi Eliezer. Hyrcanus did not come to take part in the feast. He came to complain about his son Eliezer, who had left his old father and run away to Yerushalayim. When Hyrcanus arrived in Yerushalayim and asked where he could find Rabbi Yochanan ben Zakkai, he was told, "He is having a feast in his home today." This is how Hyrcanus arrived at the house.

Rabbi Yochanan recognized Hyrcanus as the father of his *talmid* Rabbi Eliezer.

"Make room for him among the honored guests," he told his students.

Abba Hyrcanus was seated in a prominent place at the head of the table. He was trembling in surprise. "Why are they giving me so much honor?" he wondered.

Hyrcanus watched as Rabbi Yochanan told one of his students to stand up and begin to lecture on the Torah. The student was his son Eliezer!

Rabbi Eliezer arose and spoke words of Torah, beautiful words, as pleasing as the words of the Torah which the Children of Israel received on

Mount Sinai. When he finished, Rabbi Yochanan ben Zakkai got up from his seat and kissed Rabbi Eliezer.

Hyrcanus was overcome with joy and pride. He stood up and announced to all the guests, "My teachers and rabbis! I came to Yerushalayim to complain about my son. I wanted to punish him by not giving him any of my fortune! But now that I have seen what a *talmid chacham* he is, I have changed my mind. All my possessions are his. He will even get his brothers' shares."

"Father," answered Rabbi Eliezer, "if I had wanted gold and silver, I could have asked the Holy One, blessed be He, and He would have granted me riches. But I did not come here to seek money or honor. I came here because I loved the Torah. Give your treasures to my brothers. I do not deserve any more than they. I ask nothing from *Hakadosh Baruch Hu*, except to be able to study Torah."

Rabbi Eliezer remained in Yerushalayim and continued to study until he became the teacher of all Israel.

Sources: Midrash Bereshith Rabbah, chapter 42
Avoth de Rabbi Nathan, chapter 6
Pirkey de Rabbi Eliezer

The wise man and the merchants

Once a ship full of people was sailing on the high seas. It was sailing to a far-away land, and all the passengers had taken merchandise with them to sell. Some people had cloth. Others had fruit from Eretz Yisrael—almonds, raisins, and figs. Still others had expensive dishes—bowls and pitchers of gold and stained glass. Someone had carpets, and some people had jewelry—rings, bracelets and necklaces. Everyone had something valuable and expensive.

While sitting on deck, the passengers began to talk.

"I have the best merchandise of all. I will make more money from my sales than any of you!" each one boasted. Everyone showed his friends the bags and the crates, the bundles and the boxes that he was bringing with him.

There was one man on the ship who did not boast about his merchandise. He did not take part in the conversation at all. This man had a book in his hand, and all he did was read and study.

*All the passengers had taken merchandise
with them to sell.*

Love for Torah and those who study it

At first, the passengers left him alone and did not disturb him. But it was a long journey, and after each man had already told all the stories he had to tell, people became bored. Finally, one passenger turned to the man with the book and asked, "Where is your merchandise? What do you have to sell? How many chests and bundles have you brought with you on the boat?"

But this man was not a merchant. He was a learned rabbi. He thought for a while and then slowly said, "My merchandise is more important than yours, but I have hidden it and you will not be able to see it."

"Why can't we see it?" asked the passengers. "Each of us has showed his goods. Show us yours too."

"Not now. There will come a time when you will see it," the wise man replied.

The merchants searched every corner of the ship, but they couldn't find even one box or bundle belonging to the rabbi. So they laughed and said, "You don't really have anything. You are just bragging!"

The wise man just smiled.

Time passed. One day a pirate ship suddenly appeared and sailed alongside their boat. The pirates boarded the merchant ship and took all of the precious cargo—the rugs and vessels, the jewels and cloth, the fruit and all the other valuables. After they took everything away, they fled.

When the ship reached land at last, the merchants had nothing left to sell. They did not even have money to buy food. They stood on the streets of the strange city, not knowing what to do or where to turn.

The wise rabbi, on the other hand, went straight to the *beith knesseth*. He said his *tefilloth* and sat down to study Torah. The Jews in the *beith knesseth* saw that a rabbi had come from a faraway land, and they came over and greeted him. They asked him many questions, and he answered them all sensibly and well, for he was both wise and learned in the Torah.

The people saw his wisdom, and they honored and respected him. They invited him to their homes and asked him to dine with them. They gave him many gifts, and finally, they asked him to remain in the city to become their rabbi. They promised him a house and everything else he might need.

When the rabbi agreed to remain in the town, the people took him to his new home. They walked respectfully to the right and to the left of him, just as if he were a king.

Meanwhile, the merchants who had come with him on the ship were still standing about in the streets. They were hungry and miserable, but no one asked about them or offered to help them.

When they saw the rabbi walking with the people of the town, they came over and said, "Please help us, Rabbi. You remember how rich we were and how many beautiful things we had to sell until the pirates came and robbed us. Please tell the people of the city that you know us. Ask them to give us some bread, for we are hungry and we have nothing left."

The rabbi smiled and said, "Now you see that my merchandise was better than yours. The Torah which I studied and kept in my mind is the best merchandise I have. No robber can take it from me. It is because of my knowledge of Torah that I am given all this honor and respect. But don't despair. I will ask the people of the city to help you too."

On hearing the rabbi's request, the people of the town collected food and clothing, and gave money to the merchants so that they could return to their homes.

Source: Midrash Tanchuma, Trumah

10

The blessings of hard work

True satisfaction

At first, Rabbi Akiva was very poor. He could barely make a living for his family. Every day he went to the forest, chopped down a few trees and sawed them into pieces. He then bundled the wood and sold half of it, and with the money he earned, he bought food for himself and his wife and children.

What did he do with the other half of the wood? He put some of it in the oven to kindle a fire and warm the house on cold winter days. And at night, he held a piece of burning wood in his hand, so that he could sit and study the Torah by its light.

Rabbi Akiva was happiest when he studied. He loved learning so much that he forgot his poverty, and he was always cheerful and content.

Late at night, when Rabbi Akiva finally wanted to sleep, he spread some of the remaining branches on the floor and lay down to sleep, for he was so poor that he had no bed. Because he worked so hard and studied so much, he slept soundly even on the hard boards.

The blessings of hard work

Once Rabbi Akiva's neighbors came and complained.

"Akiva, we are bothered by the smoke from the wood which you burn in your house," said the neighbors. "We have a suggestion. Why don't you sell us the wood that you have left? Then you can buy some oil and a lamp. You will have better light, and we will not be bothered by smoke."

The neighbors exaggerated somewhat. They were not really bothered by the smoke. They thought that if they could make Rabbi Akiva sell them his wood and buy a lamp, he could study the Torah in better light. Rabbi Akiva understood what they wanted, but he did not agree.

"I won't sell you the boards," he said. "The wood gives me everything that my family and I need — food and warmth, light to study Torah, and a bed to sleep."

Because Rabbi Akiva was satisfied with so little then, *Hashem* later gave him great riches. So great was his wealth that he dined on tables of silver and gold, and he climbed up to his bed on golden steps.

Source: Avoth de Rabbi Nathan, chapter 6

🌿 166

The fruit of one's labors

Long ago, a Roman king named Adrianus went out to make war on his enemies in a distant land. On the way, the king and his soldiers passed through Eretz Yisrael. When he reached a small village not far from the city of Tiberias, he saw an old man working in his garden. The man, stooped with age and years of toil, was bending over and hoeing the earth. When he was finished, he dug holes in the ground and planted young fig trees. The king stopped to watch the old man at work.

The old man worked very hard. His hands were busy with the saplings, and beads of perspiration dripped down his forehead.

The king shook his head in amazement. "Haven't you worked hard enough all your life, grandfather? How old are you?" he asked.

"I am one hundred years old, Your Majesty," replied the old man.

"A man of a hundred working and bothering to plant young trees! Why must you work so hard? What good is it to plant these trees? Do you really think that you will live long enough to enjoy their fruit? You will soon die and others will enjoy the fruit of your labors!" the king said.

"No matter!" answered the old man. "If the Holy One, blessed be He, wills it, I may still live to eat the fruit of the trees that I am planting. And if not, just as I ate the fruit of the trees which my father and grandfather planted, so will my children enjoy the fruit of my labors."

The king went on his way, together with his soldiers. The war was long and drawn out. It dragged on for three years. When the fighting ended in the fourth year, the king returned the same way he had come and again passed the garden of the old man. Again the king saw the good, old grandfather standing near the fig trees which he had planted. The trees had grown in the meantime and borne sweet and luscious figs.

When the old man saw the king approaching, he hurried and took a little basket, filled it with juicy figs, and presented it to the king.

"Your Majesty," he said, "I am the old man whom you met here more than three years ago when I was planting these figs. The good Lord has kept me alive to enjoy the fruit of the trees. Here is my fruit as a gift to Your Royal Highness."

"I see that God loves you, so I will honor you too," said the king to the old man.

He turned to his servants and said, "Take the

gift from him. Put the figs in another basket and fill his basket with gold coins."

The servants did as the king commanded. They took out the figs, filled the basket with gold coins, and returned it to the old man.

The grandfather went home happy and contented. He told his wife and children and grandchildren all that had happened, and the entire family rejoiced with the hardworking old man.

Source: Midrash Tanchuma, Kedoshim

The blessings of hard work

There was once a city called Lodkia. At one time the inhabitants of that city needed a great deal of oil. They needed so much, that there was not enough oil in the whole city—not even in the entire country—to fill their needs.

The people of the city gathered together and discussed where and how to find the oil they needed. They decided that one person among them would go to Eretz Yisrael to buy oil. A wise and faithful messenger was chosen to go on the journey. He was given a big purse full of silver coins. "Buy all the oil you can get for this money," they instructed him.

The man started out on foot for Yerushalayim. He walked for many days. When he finally arrived at the city, he asked people, "Will you sell me oil for my silver?"

"No," answered the people of Yerushalayim, "we don't have that much oil. Go to the city of Tzor. You might find what you are looking for in Tzor."

The messenger went to Tzor. When he arrived, he asked the people, "Will you sell me oil for my silver?"

"No," answered the people of Tzor, "we don't have enough oil to sell to you. Go to the city of Gush-Halav. There you might find what you are seeking."

The man took to the road again, and walked many days until he reached Gush-Halav. "I have come to buy oil," he told the people. "I am ready to pay all the money that I have in my purse."

The people of Gush-Halav answered, "There is one man in this city who can sell you so much oil. Go out to the fields. You will find him there."

The messenger went out to the fields and came to a grove of olive trees. There was a man in the grove digging holes in the ground for new olive trees.

"Do you have oil to sell me?" the messenger asked the farmer. "I will pay you all the money I have in my purse. I have traveled a great distance— all the way from the city of Lodkia—to buy a large supply of oil for the people of my city."

The man looked at the stranger.

"Yes, I have enough oil and I can sell you some, but first I must finish my work in the fields," said the farmer.

The messenger watched as the man continued his work. When he finished, he put his tools on his

"Do you have oil to sell me?" the messenger
asked the farmer.

shoulders, and the two started back to the city.

On the road through the olive orchard, the farmer would stop once in a while and bend down to clear the rocks from the soil so that the trees would grow better.

The messenger was surprised. "A man who has so much oil must be very rich," he thought. "Why does he work so hard, doing everything himself? He even moves the heavy rocks in his orchard without any help. Maybe he is really a poor man and the townspeople were just making fun of me when they said I can buy oil from him."

As they approached the farmer's house, a maid came running towards the farmer holding a kettle full of warm water for him to wash his hands and face. Then she brought a golden basin filled with pure oil for him to annoint his hands and feet.

The messenger was very impressed with what he saw, and he realized that this hardworking farmer was indeed very rich.

The farmer invited the messenger to eat and drink, and after the meal, he measured out a large amount of oil for him, as much as his money could buy. Then the rich farmer asked the messenger, "Is this enough oil, or do you want more?"

"I would gladly buy more, but I don't have any more money," answered the messenger.

"It doesn't matter. You can pay me another time," the rich man said. "I will go back with you

The blessings of hard work

to your city, and you will pay me whatever you owe me there."

The messenger agreed and bought more oil. Then he hired all the horses and donkeys, all the mules and camels in Eretz Yisrael, and loaded them with all the jugs of oil he had bought.

The messenger and the wealthy farmer returned to Lodkia. When the people of Lodkia saw the long caravan approaching, they came forward to meet it with great joy. They praised the messenger and said, "There is not another man as clever and as diligent as you, for you have succeeded in bringing us all this oil."

The messenger listened to their words and said, "Do not praise me, but praise this man who has come with me. He is the one who is diligent and clever. He is so rich that he alone was able to sell me all of this oil. Just the same, he himself does all the hard work in his orchards. Although he looks poor, no one is as rich as he."

When the people of Lodkia heard this, they showed great respect and honor to this hard-working man whose labors were blessed by *Hashem*.

They paid him for the oil, and he returned to his home.

Source: Talmud Bavli, Menachoth 85b

🌹 174

Food is not for wasting

abylonia had a blessed year. The wheat grew well and the harvest was rich. Since flour was plentiful, bread was cheap and people became careless. They threw away a lot of food, and they even played games with loaves of bread.

One day, two people were standing in the marketplace and throwing bread at each other for fun. Just then, a wise man named Rabbi Yehudah passed by. When he saw the people playing with bread, he said, "It seems that we have too much food. You are so full and comfortable that you have forgotten *Hashem*'s commandment: 'Do not destroy! Do not waste food!' In such a case, it would be better to have a famine in the land, so that people will remember *Hashem* and His commandments."

Rabbi Yehudah was a righteous man, and *Hashem* made his words come true. There was no rain that year and nothing grew. No wheat or barley came up, nor were there any vegetables or fruit. The little food which was left over from the year of plenty was very expensive. People waited in long lines to buy their bread. Some went hungry, and in their trouble, they remembered with sadness and regret how they had wasted their food in times of plenty! "We wish that we now had just a little dry bread," they moaned.

Rabbi Yehudah did not know that trouble had come to the world, for he sat home all day long studying Torah and he rarely went outside. But the other rabbis saw the people suffering and they said to Rav Kahana (Rabbi Yehudah's helper), "You are always together with the *tzaddik*, Rabbi Yehudah. Take him to the marketplace so he can see how hungry the people are."

Rav Kahana asked Rabbi Yehudah to come out and walk with him. When they reached the marketplace, the rabbis saw a long line of people near the only open stall in the marketplace.

Rabbi Yehudah was surprised. "What's happening here? Why are so many people here?" he asked.

"This is the only merchant who has food to sell," the people answered. "All he has is spoiled food and peels from dates. The food is worthless, yet the hunger is so great that everyone wants to buy some."

"It seems that a famine has come to the world," said Rabbi Yehudah. "We must proclaim a fast day — a day of atonement. We must pray to

"We must pray to Hashem for mercy."

The blessings of hard work

Hashem for mercy and must ask Him to give food to the hungry people."

He turned to his servant and said, "Please take off my shoes." (On the major fast days of Yom Kippur and Tisha b'Av, we do not wear shoes.)

The servant took off the first shoe. It immediately began to rain, even before Rabbi Yehudah started to pray, because *Hashem* instantly fulfills the good wishes of a *tzaddik*.

The next day, ships loaded with rice and wheat arrived in Babylonia, and the food was divided among all the hungry people. Everyone ate and thanked *Hashem* for His kindness.

Source: Talmud Bavli, Ta'anith 24

11

Love for
God's creatures

Noach and the animals in the ark

Before *Hakadosh Baruch Hu* brought the flood upon the world, He commanded Noach to build an ark for his wife, his three sons — Shem, Cham and Yefeth — and their wives. *Hashem* also ordered him to take all the different kinds of beasts, birds and insects into the ark.

Noach obeyed God's command. He prepared a special place for each animal. He built a wide, roomy stall for the elephants, a barn for the cows, and a stable for the goats and sheep. He made sturdy cages for the lions and wolves and all other beasts of prey, so that they could not get out and hurt the cattle. He built nests for the birds, and small cages for the mice and lizards.

Noach also prepared food for all the animals, and he put it in the storehouses on the ark. He prepared the proper food for each animal — straw and hay for the camels; grasses for the deer and cows; barley for the horses and donkeys; branches and leaves for the elephants; and seeds for the birds.

Love for God's creatures

But the real work began for Noach and his sons when the waters rose and the ark was finally afloat. They had to take care of all the animals and to bring each one its food. Each animal had to be fed at the proper time. The lions, the tigers, and the wolves ate at night. The chickens and birds wanted their meals during the day. One animal ate at one o'clock, another at two o'clock, and a third at three o'clock.

Day and night, Noach, Shem, Cham and Yefeth were busy feeding the animals. Many times they themselves did not get a chance to eat or rest. For how could they leave the poor hungry animals unfed in their cages?

Once, Noach was late bringing food to the lion. The lion was hungry and upset, and he roared a loud and terrible roar. Noach heard the noise and was frightened. "I have not yet fed the lion tonight!" he exclaimed. He ran and brought a chunk of meat to the angry beast. But the lion was in such a rage that he struck Noach with his huge paw and hurt his leg. From that time on, Noach limped and it was hard for him to walk.

Nevertheless, he continued to take care of the animals. Even when Noach, Shem, Cham and Yefeth were very tired and hungry, they would neither eat nor sleep until they had fed all the animals.

Except for one. Noach did not know what to

feed the chameleon, a lizard-like animal that changes its colors. The chameleon sat in his narrow cage and stared at Noach sadly, not knowing how to show what food he needed. Noach felt very sorry for the chameleon. He offered him grass and seeds, meat and fruit of all kinds. But the chameleon remained in a corner without moving, and Noach was afraid that it would die.

But *Hashem* helped the chameleon because He wanted all the animals on the ark to remain alive. One day Noach was standing next to the chameleon's cage, slicing a pomegranate for himself. (He didn't have time to sit down at a table and to eat his own meals in leisure.) The pomegranate was wormy, and one worm fell down on the ground in front of the chameleon's cage. The chameleon quickly stuck out his long tongue, caught the worm, and ate it.

Noach was very pleased.

"So you like to eat worms?" he said. "From now on, you, too, will have food!"

From that day on, he saved all the wormy fruits and vegetables, and the chameleon never went hungry again.

Noach and his sons worked in the ark all year long. Finally *Hakadosh Baruch Hu* had pity on them and ended the flood. Slowly the waters went down and the earth was dry again.

Noach was happy that the animals would now

be able to go out and find their own food, and the animals were even happier. They wanted to be free to get their food from the hands of *Hashem*, not from the hands of man.

Sources: Midrash Tanchuma, Noach
Talmud Bavli, Sanhedrin 108b

David
the loyal shepherd

When David Hamelech (King David) was a boy, he took care of his father's herds. Every day he took the goats and sheep to the empty desert so that they would not graze in other people's fields.

David noticed that the stronger, healthier goats pushed the weaker animals aside, and ate all of the new grass themselves. They left only hard stubble for the little goats to eat.

"The little goats who don't have strong teeth should have the tender, new grass. The bigger goats can eat the stubble," David thought to himself.

What did he do? He built fences and made three separate pens — one for the little kids, one for the older goats, and one for the strong young goats.

Early each morning David opened the young kids' pen. They ran around and chewed the ends of the new, soft grass until they were satisfied. Next he took out the older goats from their pen, and they ate the regular grass that was neither hard nor soft. Last of all, he opened the pen of the sturdy young goats. They ate what was left—the hard stubble and the thick roots which they could chew with their strong teeth. All the animals were satisfied. None pushed the other to get their food, and they all got what they needed.

Hakadosh Baruch Hu saw this and said, "Let the one who cares so well for each and every one of his sheep come and be the shepherd of My sheep—the people of Israel!"

Therefore, *Hashem* chose David to be king over all of Israel.

Source: Shemoth Rabbah 2

The donkey that kept the mitzvoth

abbi Chanina ben Dosa had a donkey who grew up in his barnyard and whose job it was to carry the rabbi on his back. One day the donkey was grazing in the field when some robbers passed by. When they saw the big, strong donkey, they said to each other, "Let's take this beast of burden. We can use him to carry our sacks of stolen goods on his back!"

They tied a rope to the donkey's neck and pulled him along to their hiding place inside a big courtyard. But when they reached the courtyard, they noticed that the donkey lowered his head and looked very unhappy.

"He is probably hungry or thirsty," thought the robbers. They brought him some barley, but the donkey refused to eat. They brought him some water, but the donkey refused to drink. "Maybe he is used to eating better, softer barley," said the robbers. They tried to give him better food — but the donkey would not touch it.

For three days and three nights, the poor

donkey stood in the courtyard. He wouldn't eat a single grain because he did not want to eat from the thieves' barley. He was afraid it was stolen or that *ma'aser*—a tenth portion which must be given to the *kohanim* and the poor—had not been taken from it.

"What are we going to do with this donkey?" asked one of the robbers. "He refuses to eat and he doesn't drink! He's probably sick and will die before long. Let's get rid of him!"

The robbers removed the rope from the donkey's neck and took him out of the courtyard. "Get out of here!" they shouted.

The donkey was very weak from not eating, but he was so happy to be free that he quickly started walking. He walked all night long. In the morning he came to his master's yard. It was very early, and the barnyard gate was closed because the people in the house were still asleep. So the donkey stood outside and cried and brayed as if to say, "Please open the gate for me! I am hungry and tired!"

Rabbi Chanina ben Dosa's son heard the donkey braying and said to his father, "That donkey sounds like our donkey which was stolen!"

"Yes, it does," answered Rabbi Chanina ben Dosa. "It is indeed our donkey! Run and open the gate for him. For three days and three nights he has not eaten, and he hardly has any strength left."

Rabbi Chanina's son ran to open the gate and let the donkey into the barnyard. How miserable he looked, so thin and so weak!

They brought him a sack of barley and he ate it all. They brought him a pail full of water and he drank it all.

The donkey was happy to be back in the household of the righteous Rabbi Chanina ben Dosa and to work again for his beloved master.

Source: Avoth de Rabbi Nathan, chapter 8

God's mercy for all His creatures

Rabbi Yehudah was the leader of Israel. He was a righteous and holy man, and the people loved him. Because of their love for him, they called him "our holy rabbi" or simply "Rabbi" for short.

Hakadosh Baruch Hu also loved the saintly rabbi. And yet, once, when he was not kind to an animal, *Hashem* immediately showed him that he had not acted in the proper manner.

This is what happened:

Every day Rabbi sat in the *beith knesseth* and taught Torah to the many students who came to him. One day, it was very warm, so Rabbi sat outside, in front of the *beith knesseth*, with his pupils. He was thinking only about the words of the Torah and did not pay attention to what was happening in the street.

Just then, some people passed by. They were coming from the village and were pulling a little calf after them. The people were taking the calf to be slaughtered by the butcher. They wanted the meat for a big family feast.

When they came close to the *beith knesseth*, the calf suddenly broke loose and fled. He ran for protection to Rabbi Yehudah and hid under his wide coat. From its hiding place, the frightened animal mooed and cried, as if to say, "Please save me!"

But Rabbi did not show any pity for the calf. He pulled it out from under the folds of his coat.

"What can I do for you?" he said. "Go to the butcher! You were made for this purpose! Cows and calves were created so that people would have meat to eat!"

Hakadosh Baruch Hu saw this and said, "It is not fitting for such a wise and righteous man to behave this way! Because he showed no pity for the calf, I will not show any mercy to him. From now on he will have great pain."

That day Rabbi started to have terrible tooth-aches. For thirteen years he suffered, and no doctor was able to cure him, because such was God's wish.

One day, when Rabbi Yehudah's housekeeper was cleaning, she found some newborn mice in a corner of a room. They were so tiny that they could not run away, so she took a broom to sweep them outside.

Rabbi saw what the housekeeper was about to do.

"Leave them alone!" he said. "They, too, have

191 �

a mother who will be sad if she does not find her little children. It is written in *Sefer Tehillim*, 'And His mercies are over all His creatures.' *Hashem* pities all the living things which He has created, even if they are as small and as helpless as these mice!''

Hakadosh Baruch Hu heard this and said, "Rabbi Yehudah has shown pity to animals which men usually destroy. Now I will show kindness to him."

Hashem cured Rabbi Yehudah, and from that day onward, he had no more toothaches.

Sources: Talmud Bavli, Bava Metzia 71
Midrash Bereshith Rabbah 33